KT-224-427

I.Q. Puzzles

Lagoon Books, London

Series Editor: Heather Dickson
Page design and layout: Linley Joy Clode
Cover design and illustrations: Gary Inwood Studios

Published by:
LAGOON BOOKS
PO BOX 311, KT2 5QW, UK

ISBN: 1899712682

Printed in Singapore.

Introduction

Adapted from "IQ the Logic Puzzle Game", the 70 puzzles in this book have been designed to both test and tease. Some you will find relatively easy; others might torment you for days before you are able to solve them. But remember, the visual element in every puzzle is vital – so open your eyes wide and look hard before guessing the answers (provided at the back of the book).

Whether you read the book alone or with others is up to you – it can be dipped into when the mood takes you or, for a more competitive edge, read the puzzles out loud to friends who can take turns to guess the answers.

For the ultimate mental workout, why not set a timer and try answering the questions against the clock?

To unearth the genius within you, turnover...

Matchstick Tricks

How would you arrange three matches on top of three wine glasses so that they would support a pile of coins?

Sheep

The unfortunate Farmer Giles had nine sheep in his pen, when one of them became ill with a highly infectious disease. Not knowing which animals were infected he wanted to place all the sheep in isolation, but only had two smaller square pens which he could use. How did he manage it?

Dinner Party

At a dinner party given by John and his wife Sue, a bottle of red wine was knocked over. Three couples – James and Kate, Peter and Helen, and David and Jennie – joined John and Sue at the table. From these clues can you work out whose evening-wear was ruined when the wine was spilled?

— Each man sat across from a woman.

— Each man sat between a man and a woman.

— No partners sat opposite each other.

— The host sat on the victim's right.

— James sat next to the hostess.

— Helen sat next to the victim's partner.

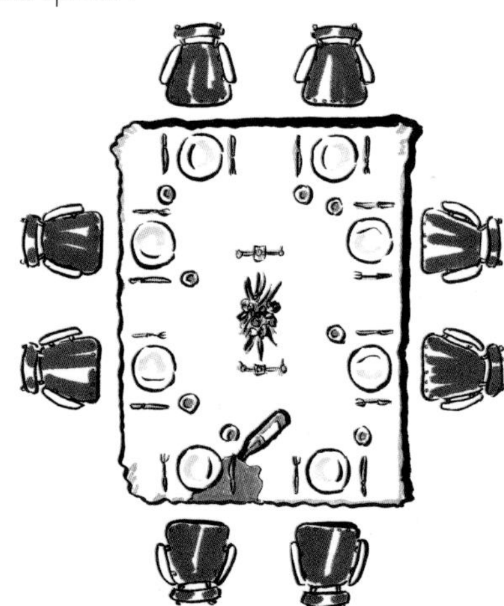

Caged Cats

Malcolm the zoo keeper has four extremely rare and dangerous big cats in his care, each living in one of four cages in a row. The cages are made from 13 separate units of bars. One night, the lion who lived in the cage at one end made a bid for freedom, and broke down the outside bars of his cage. Thankfully the keeper was watching and managed to calm the lion before he escaped from the zoo or endangered the public. Now Malcolm needs to work out how he can retain his four pens with only twelve units of bars – can you help?

Prison Poser

The cells in this prison are arranged around a central space so that the warden can keep an eye on the inmates. The prison governor wants to rearrange the prisoners so that there are four prisoners along each side. How does the warden get round this problem?

Robotics

Robbo the robotic waiter is programmed by the barman to reach his customer by following a particular sequence of coloured squares on the carpet. Part of his route is shown. Which customer is he taking the drink to?

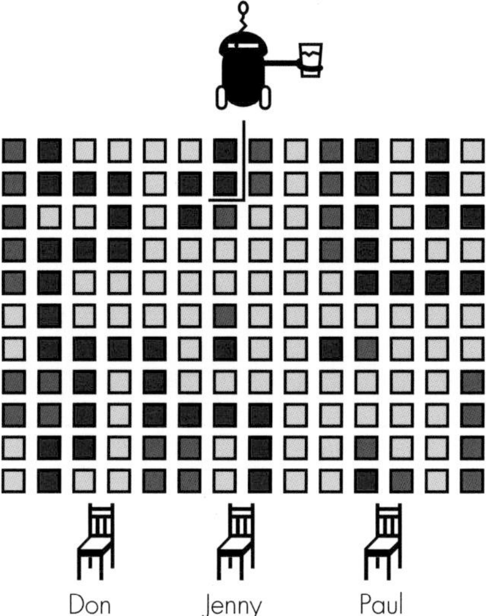

Shop 'Til You Drop

Three friends spend a shameful amount of money on shoes, handbags, hats and scarves during one brief but expensive visit to New York. Joanna was determined not to reveal to her husband how much she had spent, but from the information below he was able to work it out for himself. What did she spend?

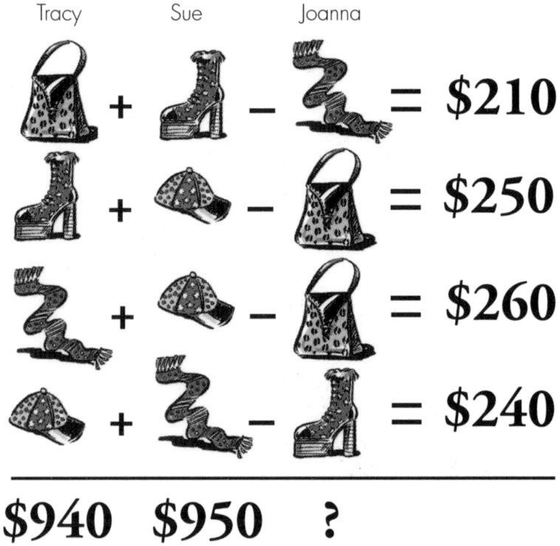

Tracy Sue Joanna

+ – = $210

+ – = $250

+ – = $260

+ – = $240

$940 $950 ?

Squares Before Your Eyes

After a challenging game of draughts, Tim said to the victorious Suzy, "Well I bet you can't tell me how many squares there are in total on this draughts board!" Help Suzy prove Tim wrong by working out how many squares there are.

Name The Gnome

Each gnome is named for a particular reason which is to do with his suit and hat. Can you discover the name of the fifth fellow?

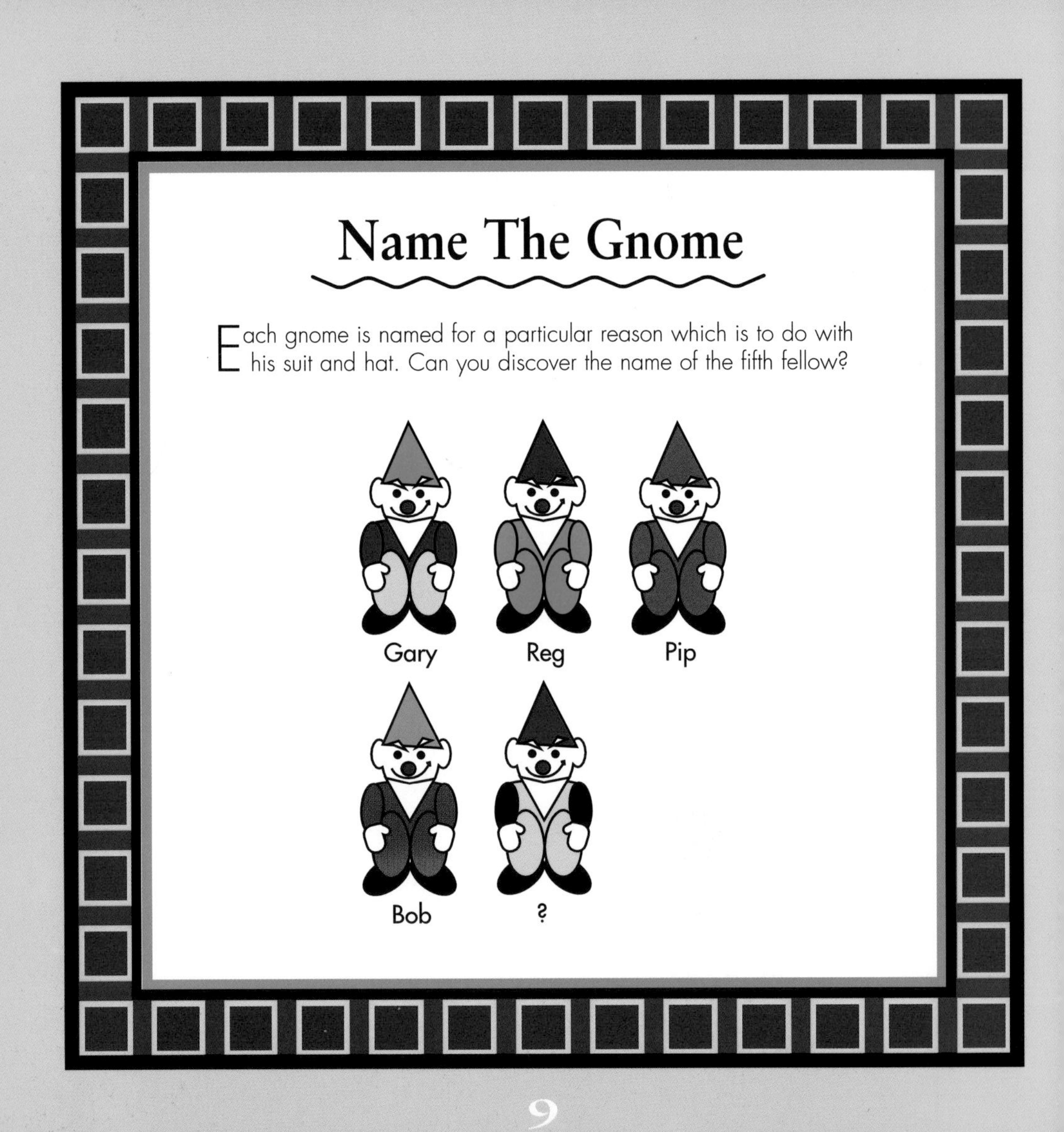

Cubed

Which of these four flattened cubes matches the one below?

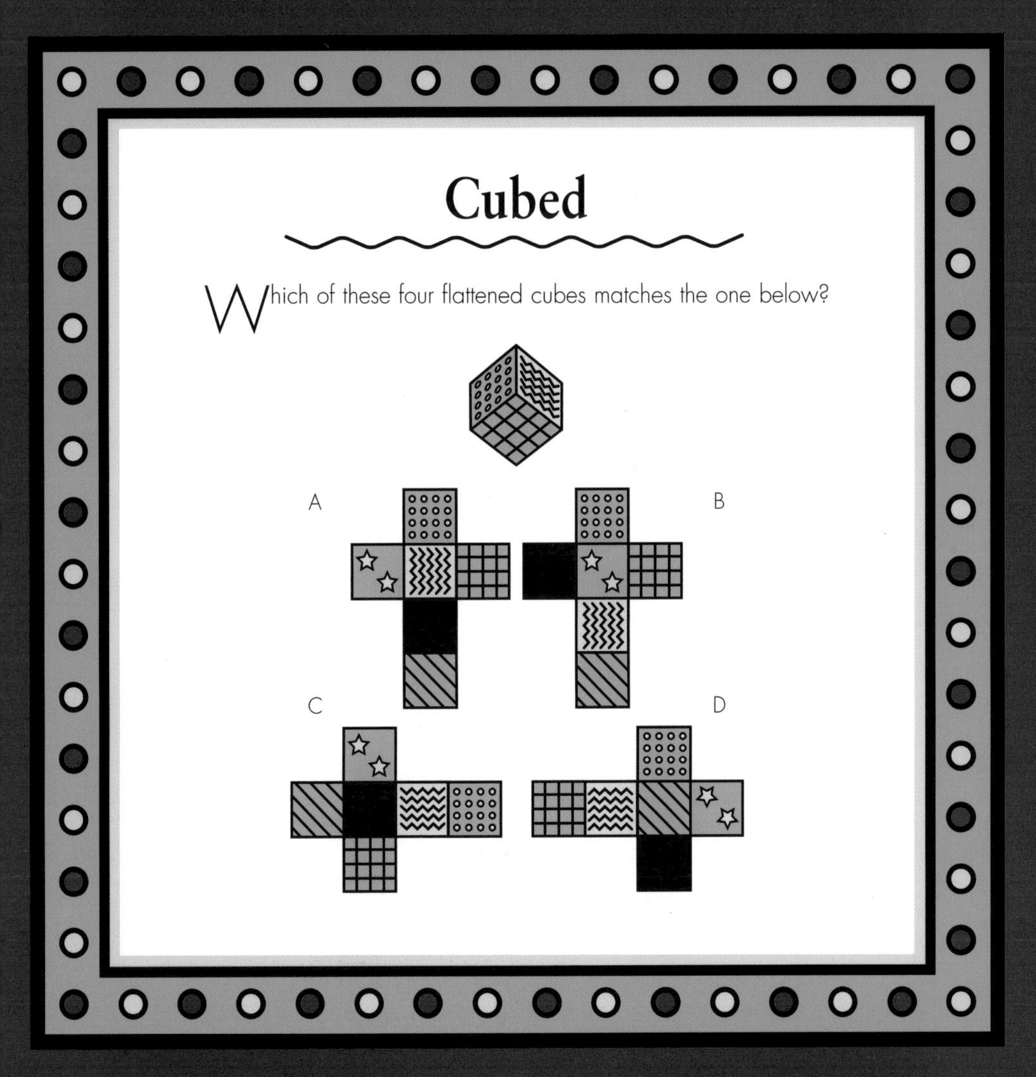

Footie Fanatics

Four friends from different parts of town plan to meet at a football match. They all leave at the same time, using different methods of transport. Jim travels by bus, Jack by car, Fred cycles and Steve walks. Given their average speeds, who arrives first?

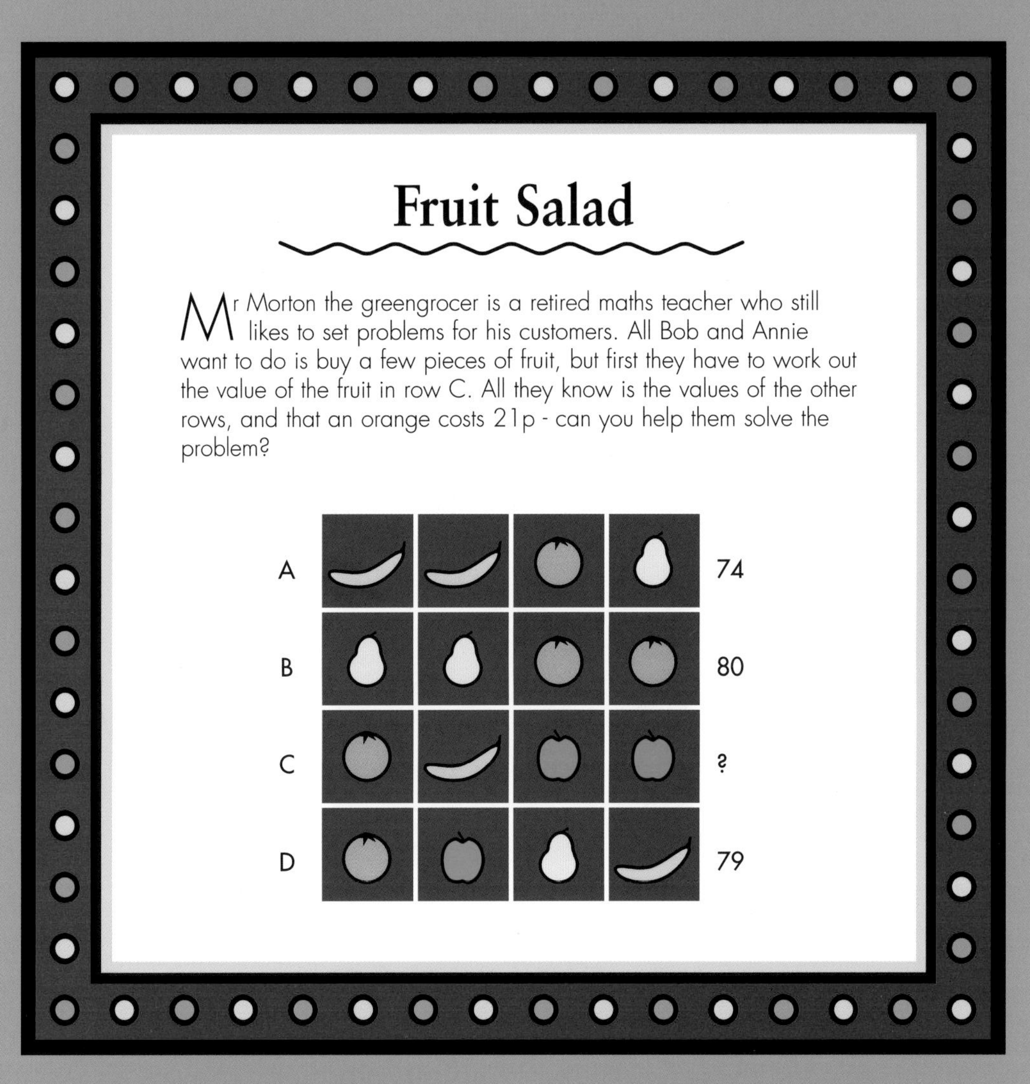

Fruit Salad

Mr Morton the greengrocer is a retired maths teacher who still likes to set problems for his customers. All Bob and Annie want to do is buy a few pieces of fruit, but first they have to work out the value of the fruit in row C. All they know is the values of the other rows, and that an orange costs 21p - can you help them solve the problem?

Snookered

Where is the best point for the white ball to hit the cushion on the snooker table, so as to hit the red and get out of this difficult situation in the most effective way?

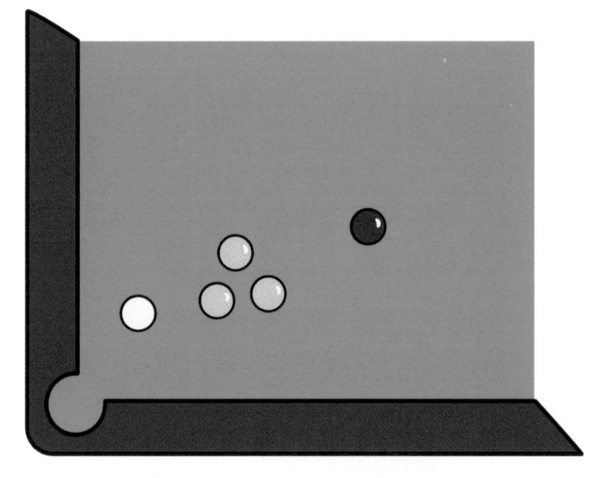

Crack The Code

A B C

D E F

Choose the tile from above that will complete the pattern below.

?

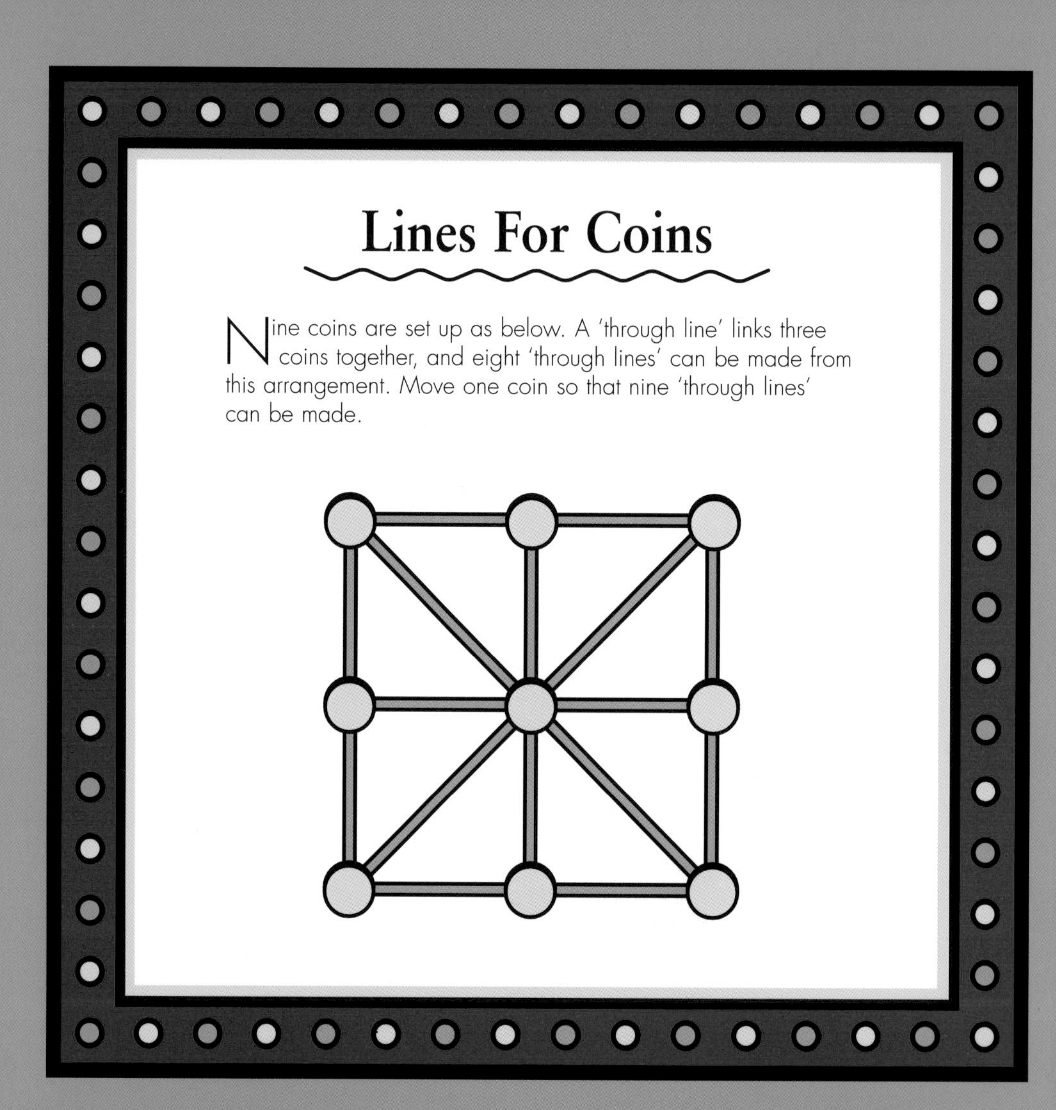

Lines For Coins

Nine coins are set up as below. A 'through line' links three coins together, and eight 'through lines' can be made from this arrangement. Move one coin so that nine 'through lines' can be made.

Name That Card

Work out the sequence and name the card that has been turned over.

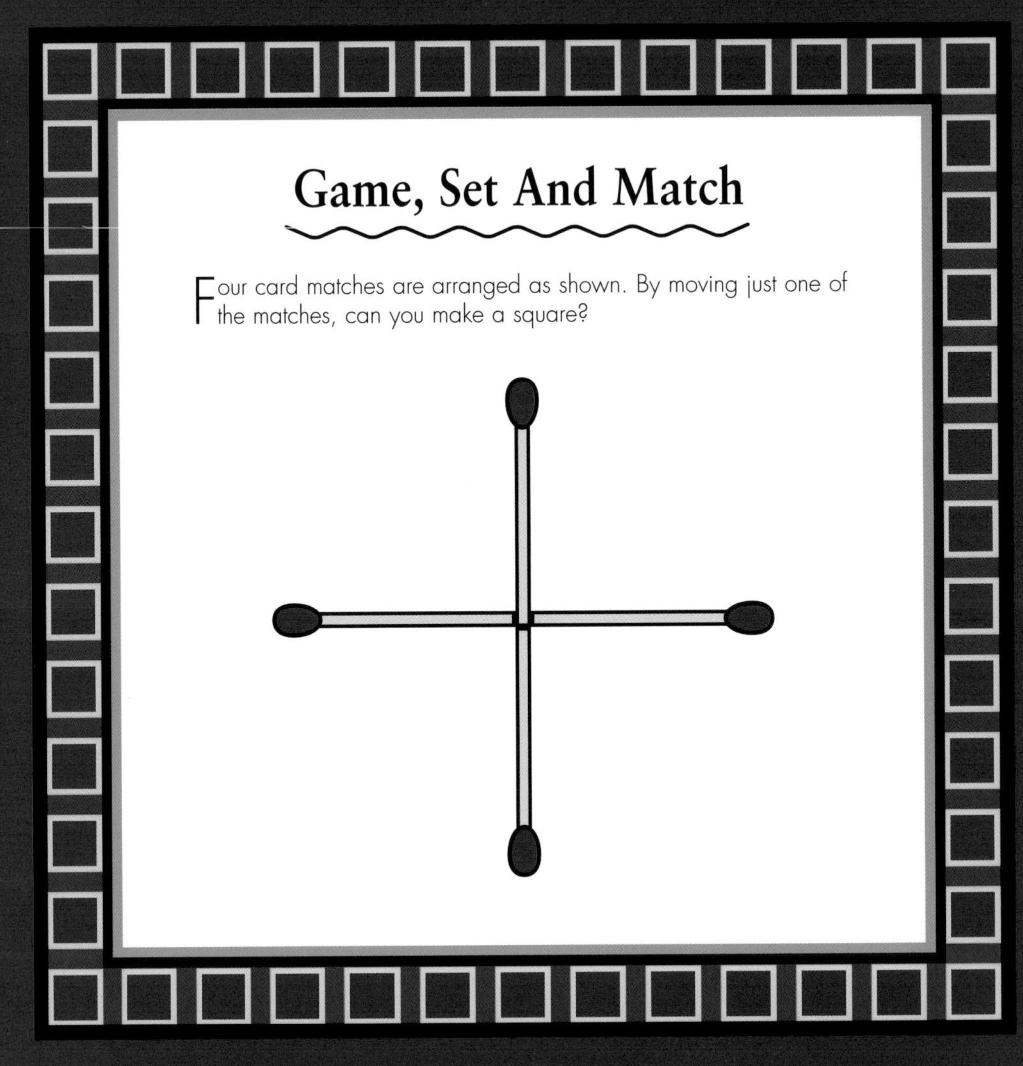

Game, Set And Match

Four card matches are arranged as shown. By moving just one of the matches, can you make a square?

Hard Currency

Bill is on holiday on the island of Etaku, a sun-and-sand resort that offers its guests all they need within one complex. After a day on the beach, Bill fancied a long, cold beer.

He handed the barman and received in change.

If equals 10 pence, and given the other information below, how much did Bill's beer cost?

Four Towns

Four towns, Portchester, Winton, Crowford, and Starham, are situated at the corners of a ten mile square. The inhabitants want to build roads to link each town, but the budget is tight and to avoid overspending they must choose the option that uses the least amount of road. Which one should it be?

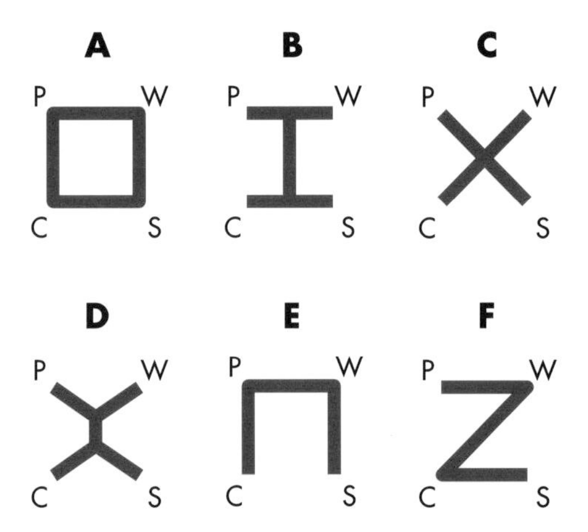

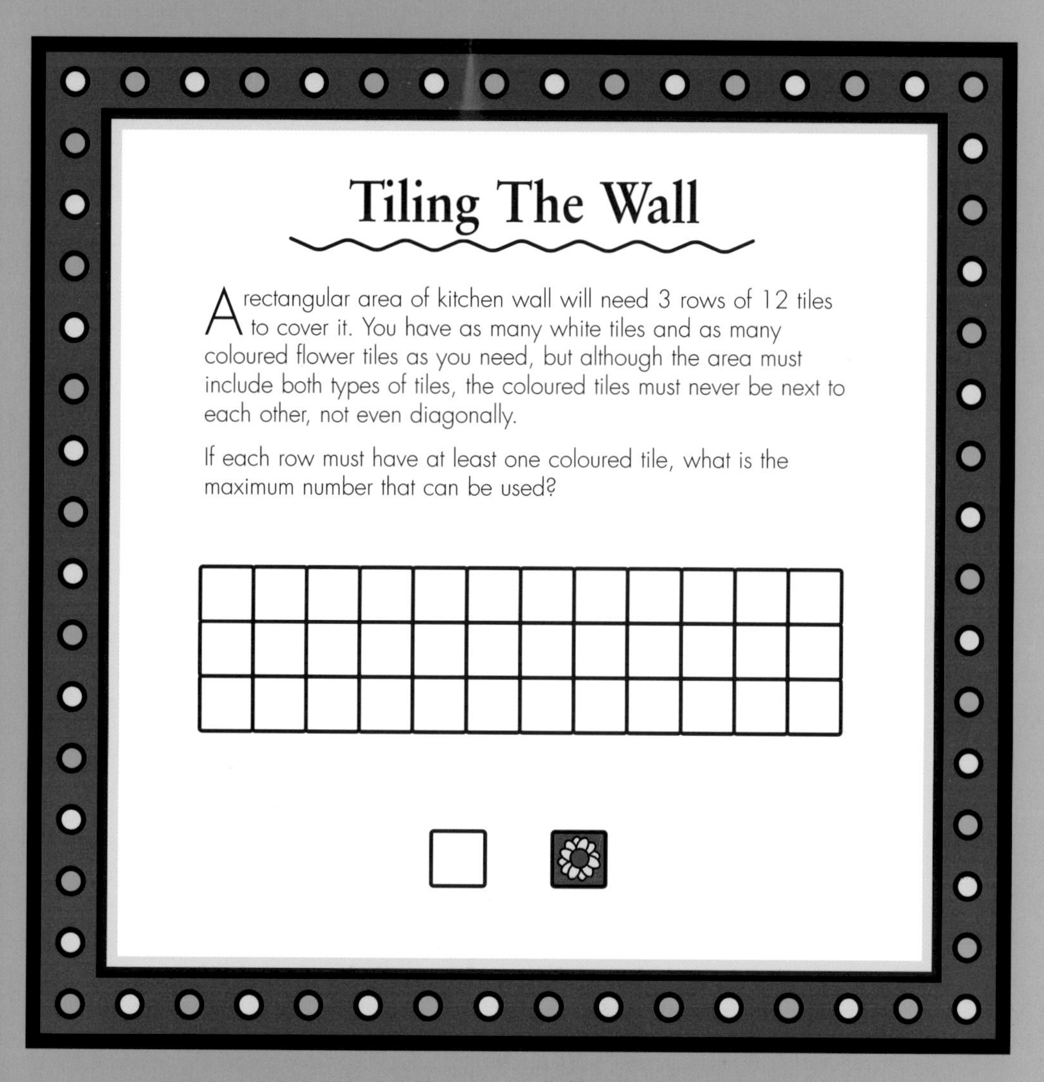

Tiling The Wall

A rectangular area of kitchen wall will need 3 rows of 12 tiles to cover it. You have as many white tiles and as many coloured flower tiles as you need, but although the area must include both types of tiles, the coloured tiles must never be next to each other, not even diagonally.

If each row must have at least one coloured tile, what is the maximum number that can be used?

A Fruity Number

Granny Smith's garden is covered in fallen pears. Can you work out how many of the pears have been eaten by the little boy next door?

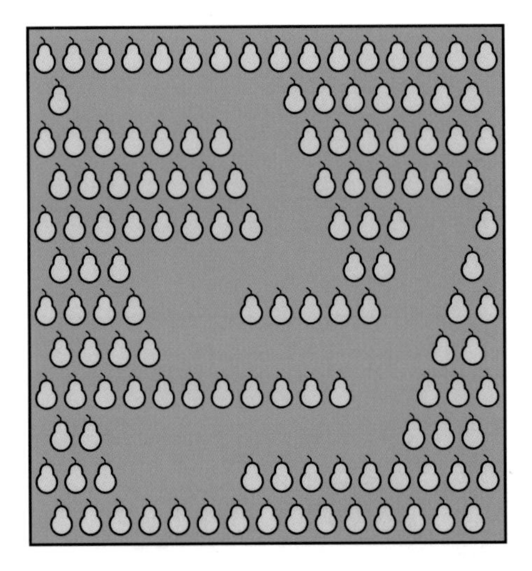

Cabbage Conundrums

Mr Till is very proud of his garden, especially his vegetable patch, and in particular his cabbages.

His cabbage patch is arranged as shown at the moment, but he would like to change their configuration so that he has twelve rows of five cabbages in each row.

Unfortunately he is no mathematician and needs your help to rearrange his cabbage patch. Can you help him?

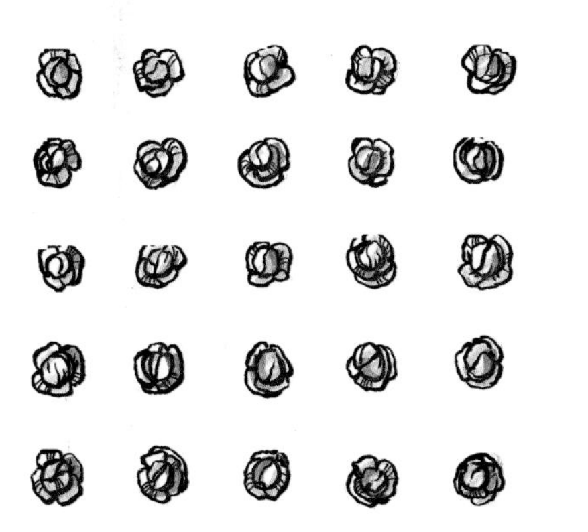

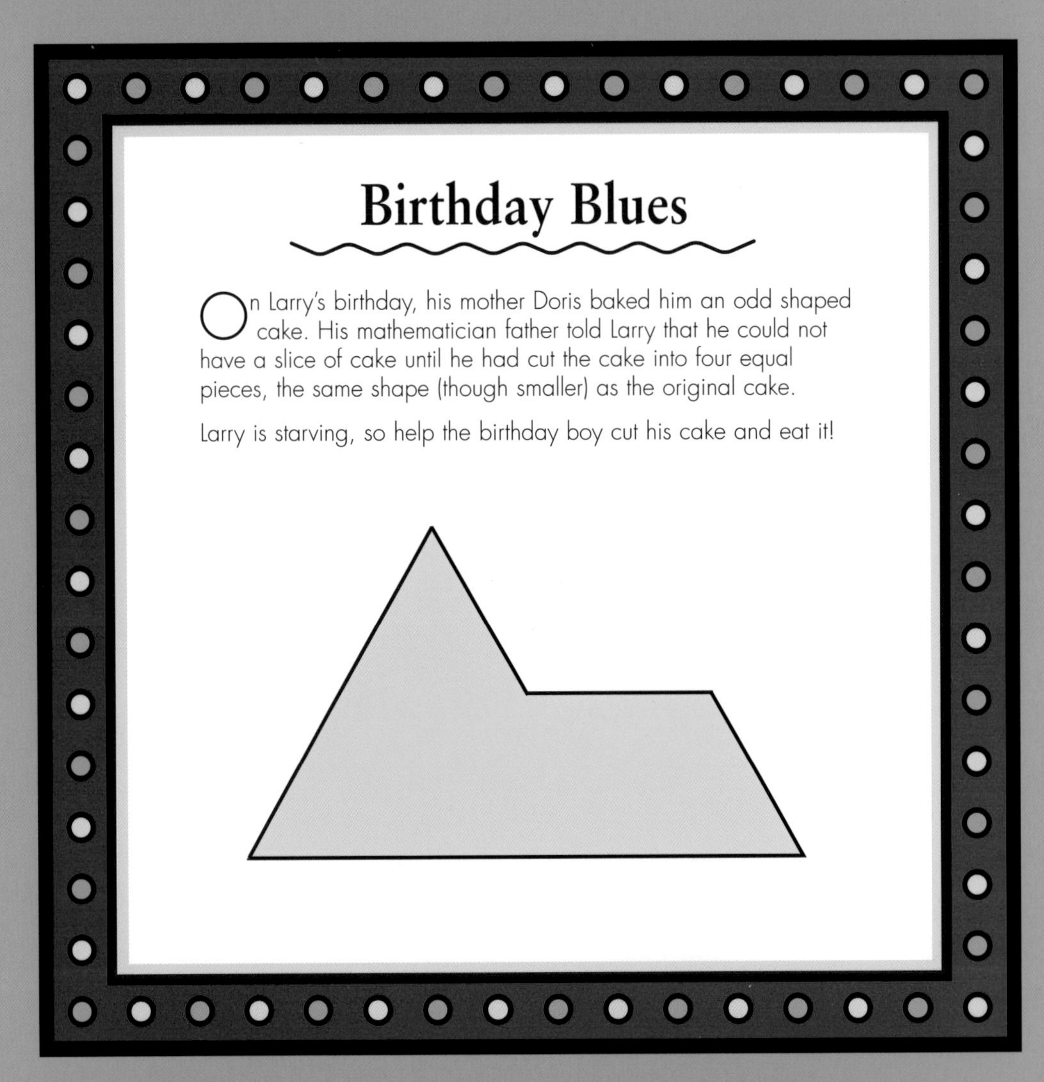

Birthday Blues

On Larry's birthday, his mother Doris baked him an odd shaped cake. His mathematician father told Larry that he could not have a slice of cake until he had cut the cake into four equal pieces, the same shape (though smaller) as the original cake.

Larry is starving, so help the birthday boy cut his cake and eat it!

Remove The Weight

The scales hold three weights in the left-hand pan which all weigh 3lbs, and exactly balance the two weights, 8lb and 1lb, in the right-hand pan.

By moving just one weight at a time from one side to the other and either adding or removing a weight, what is the smallest number of steps needed to remove the 8lb weight from the scales, leaving them balanced after each step?

You may use as many 1, 2, 3, 4, 5 and 6lb weights as you need.

Ice And A Slice

This diagram represents a cocktail glass (made here from four straws), and a slice of lemon.

Can you put the slice of lemon into the glass moving only two straws?

The Green Jigsaw Puzzle

The partly completed jigsaw puzzle shown below is made up from 16 pieces.

Which one of the five pieces does not belong?

Water Lilies

A round pond has 10 lily-pads floating in it. The owner of the pond, a research scientist, wants to divide it into 10 sections so that he can study 10 different types of fresh-water fish, but each section needs its lily-pad. He has only three circular dividers - can you work out how to do this?

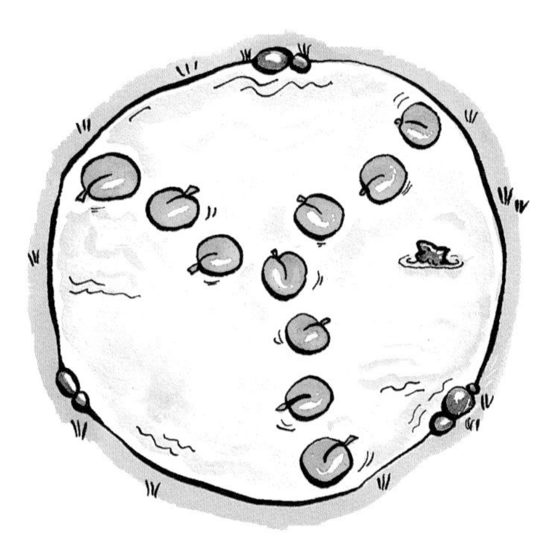

Chop Suey

How can you arrange six chopsticks so that each one touches all of the others?

Hexamania

How many regular hexagons can you count within this shape?

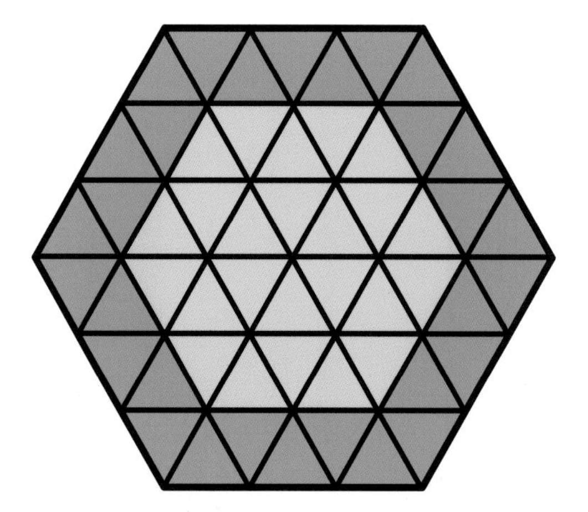

Multi-dots

In the circle below is a series of numbers. Can you work out what number should go in place of the question mark?

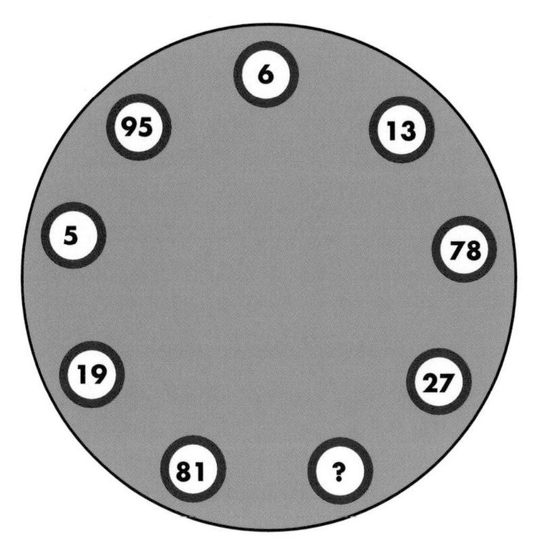

Crazy Cogs

Wheels A, B, C and D are connected with belts as shown. If wheel A rotates clockwise, can all four wheels rotate?

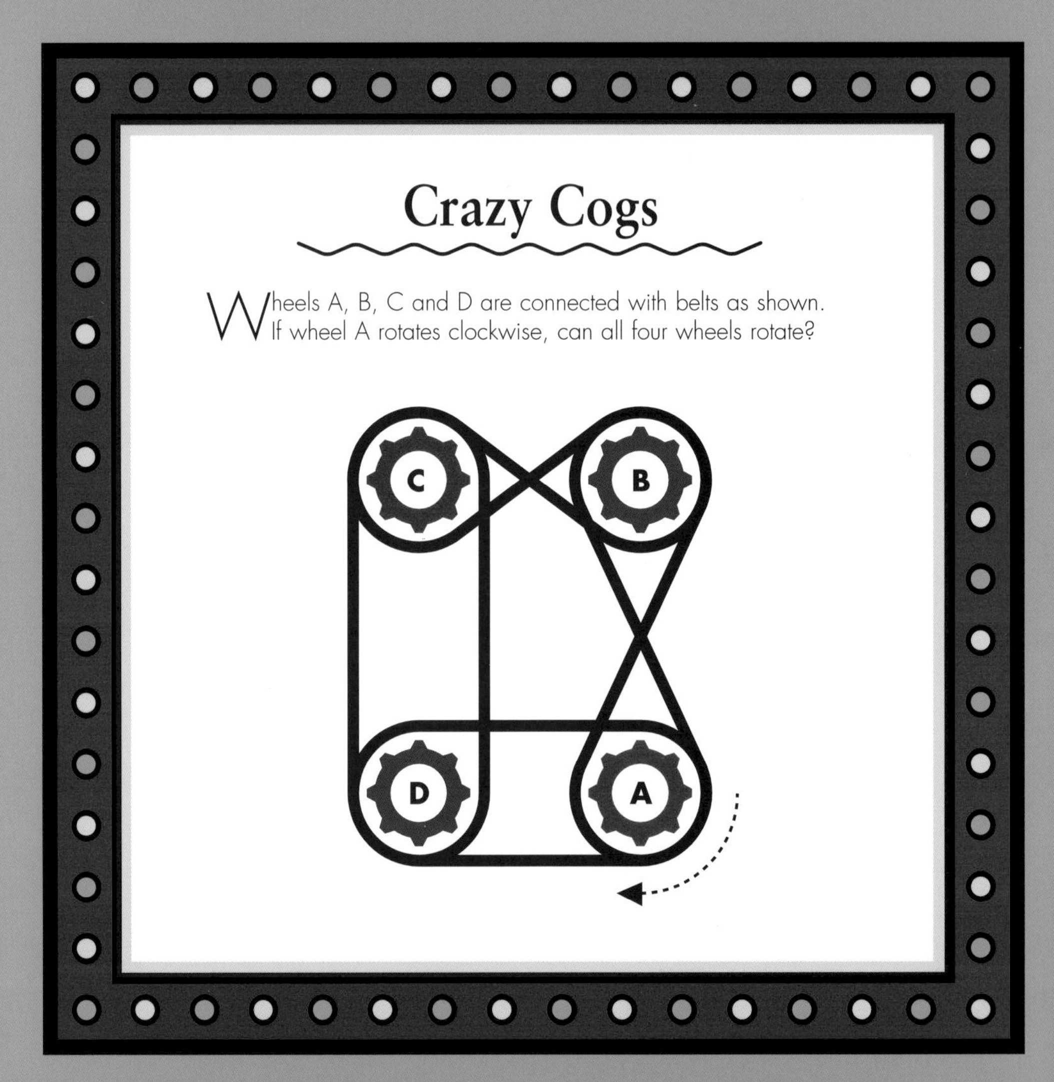

Crown Jewels

Amanda and Sarah persuaded their boyfriends to spend a fortune on jewellery when they went on a Saturday shopping expedition. James and Jerry spent £207 and £211 respectively – their friend John who had tagged along for fun, does not have a girlfriend, but if he had, he would have bought her a necklace, a ring and two pairs of earrings. How much has he saved himself by being young, free and single?

James	Jerry	John (would have bought)	
			£156
			£161
			£149
			£156
£207	£211	**?**	

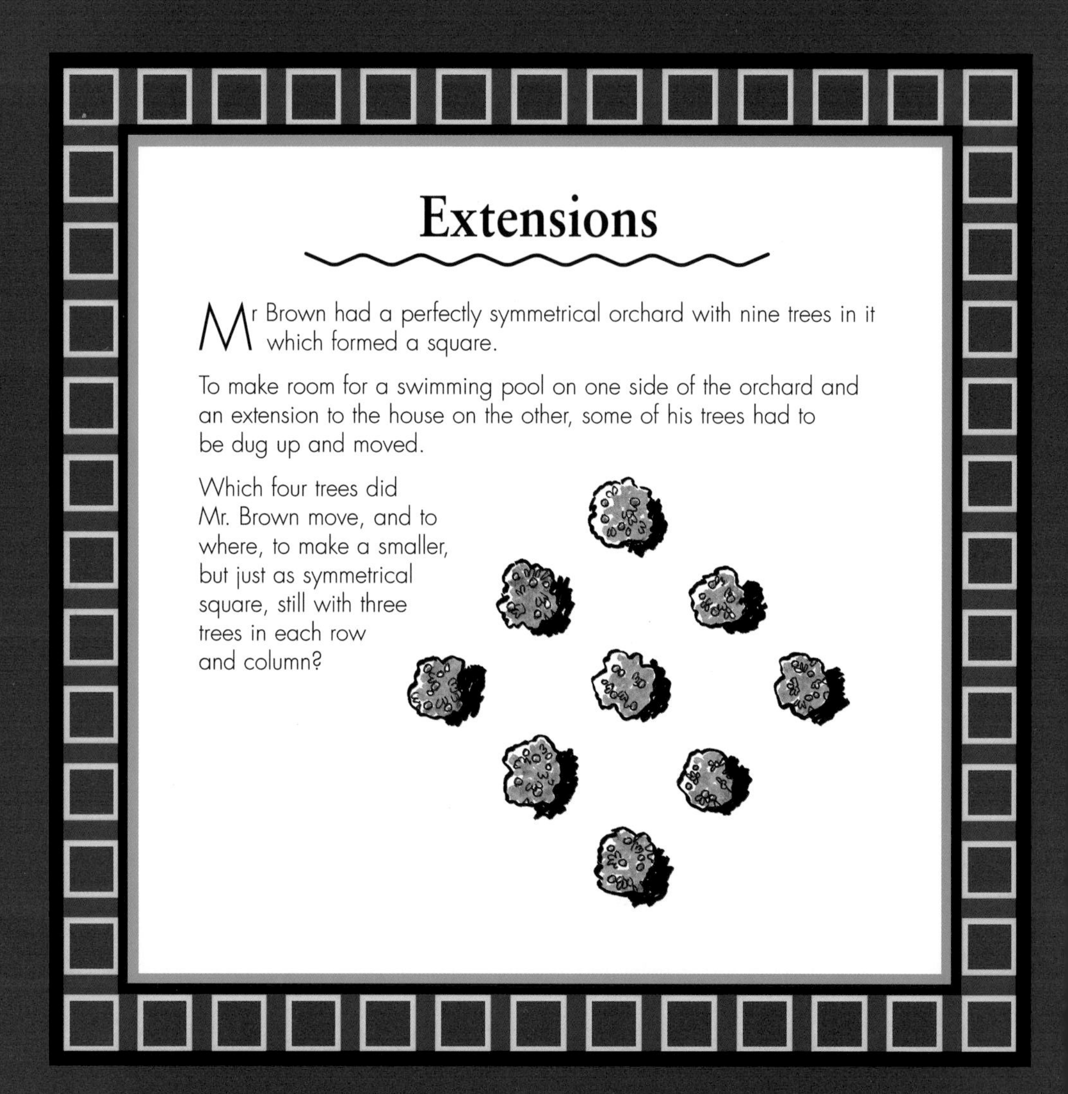

Extensions

Mr Brown had a perfectly symmetrical orchard with nine trees in it which formed a square.

To make room for a swimming pool on one side of the orchard and an extension to the house on the other, some of his trees had to be dug up and moved.

Which four trees did Mr. Brown move, and to where, to make a smaller, but just as symmetrical square, still with three trees in each row and column?

Pipe Work

Fit the nine sections of pipe into the squares so that water will flow through all nine squares and out of the tap. What section of pipe goes into the top middle square?

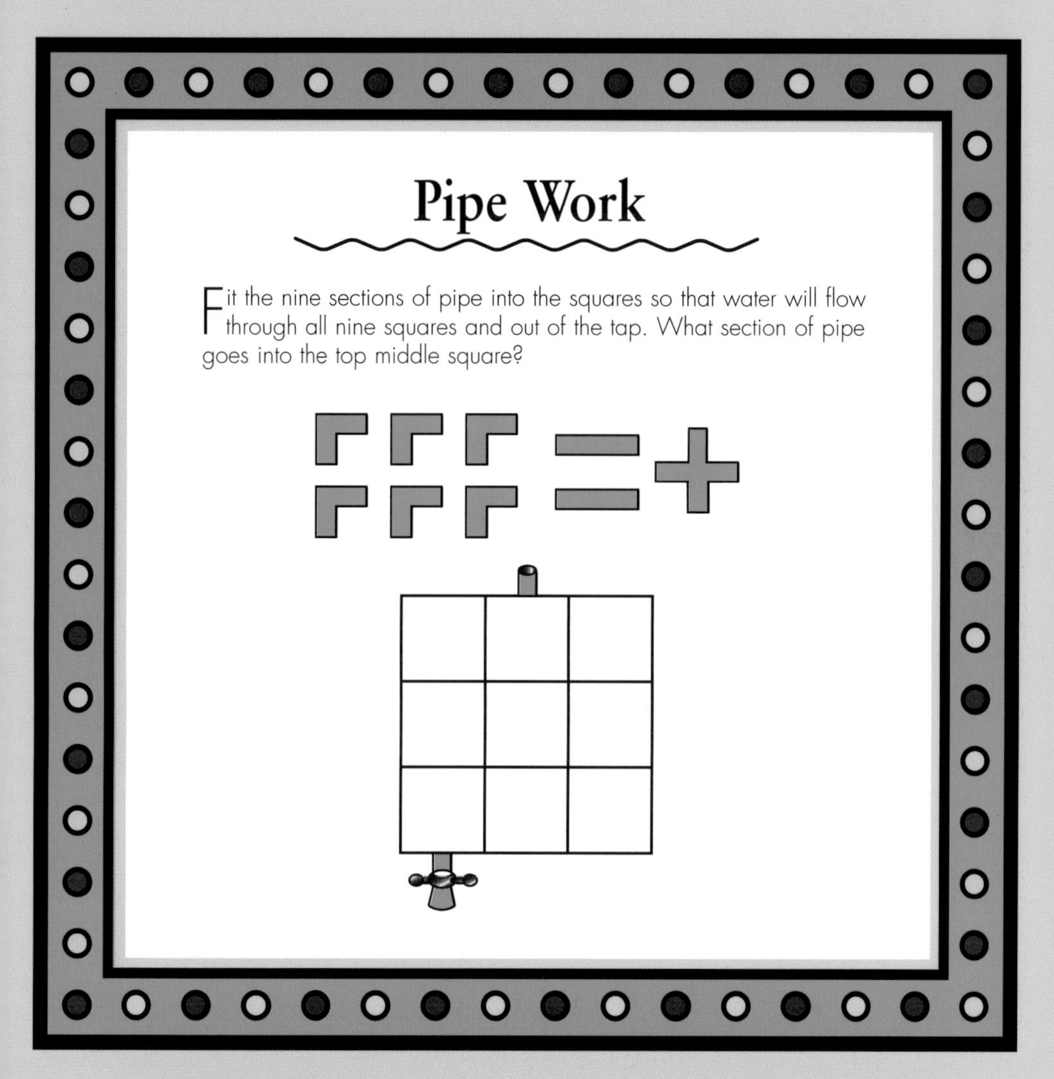

Four Knights Move

From their starting positions on the board below right, what is the least number of moves it would take for all four knights to end up on the square marked?

The knight can move three squares in an 'L' shape as in the diagram below left.

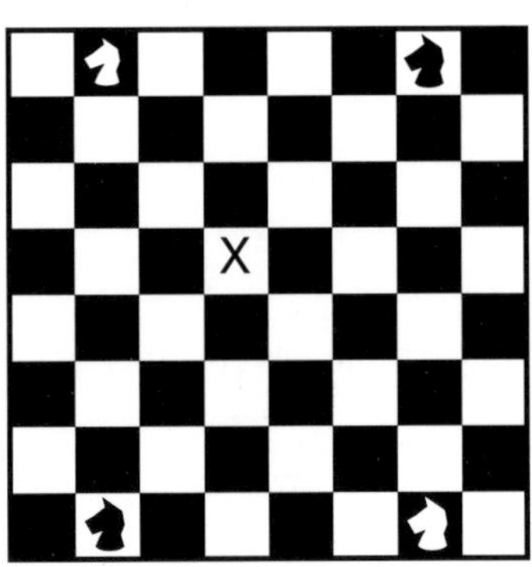

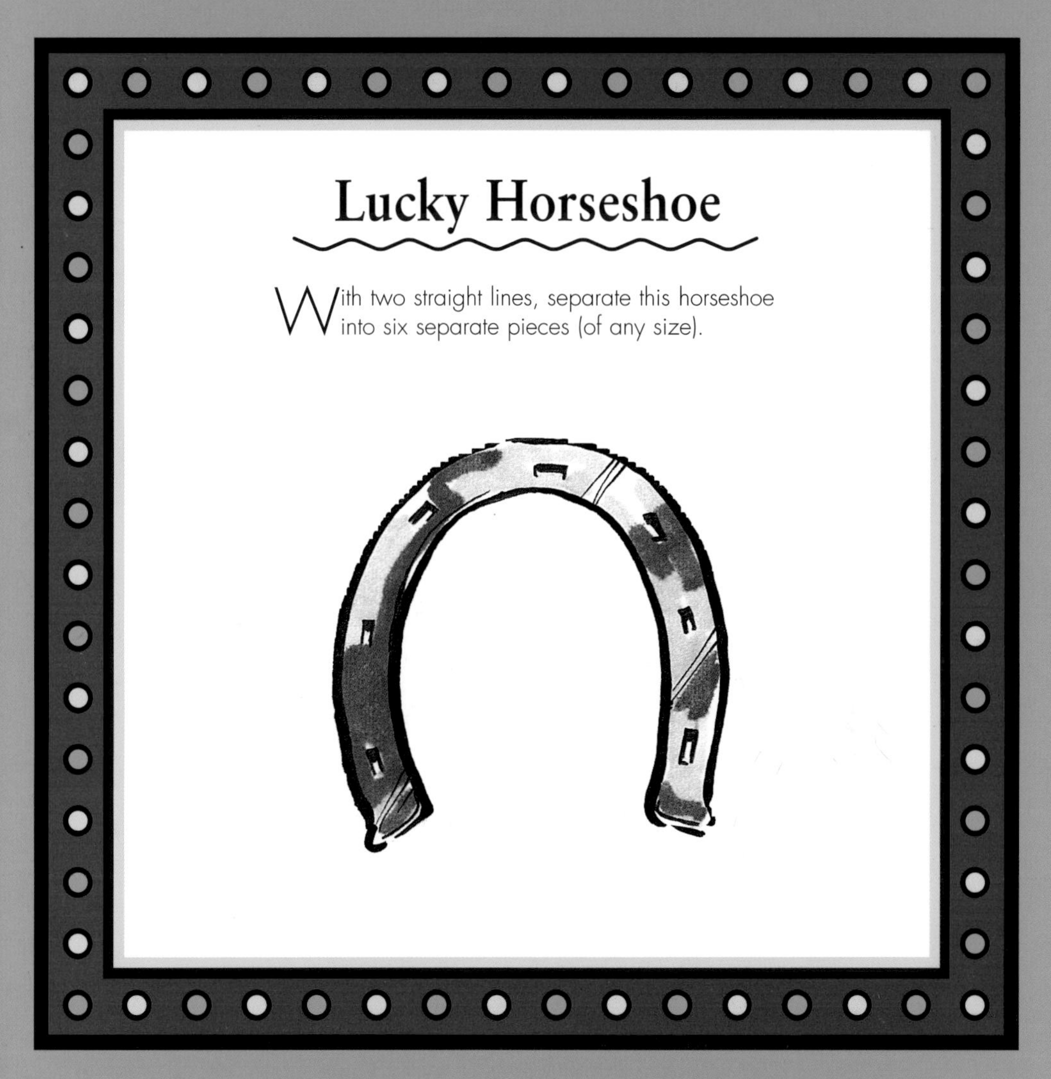

Lucky Horseshoe

With two straight lines, separate this horseshoe into six separate pieces (of any size).

Water Trough

In a field is a large water trough which needs to be emptied of its 60 litres of water so that it can be moved. There are three bungs in the trough. You can either undo two bungs which are 10cm in diameter each, or one bung which is 20cm in diameter, but you cannot open all three, or one of each size. Which should you open to empty the water as quickly as possible?

Mole

The naughty boys of IVb were fed up with Mole revealing all their exploits to the Headmaster and plotted his come-uppance. Although they wrote in code and were careful never to discuss details, Mole somehow managed to get hold of a message that revealed the time and place of an ambush. For all his skill as a spy, the code eluded him and all he worked out was that Z = A, and M = N.

Where and when did Mole come to a sticky end?

1 R	M	■	2 G	S	V
3 H	K	L	I	G	H
■	4 S	Z	O	O	■
5 Z	U	G	V	I	■
■	6 O	F	M	X	S

Chain Reaction

Class 2b are making paper-chains for their Christmas decorations. One of their circular chains for the tree has broken into four pieces. Can they join them together again by breaking and re-joining just three links?

Square The Circle

If the squares in both A and B are exactly the same size, what is the relationship between the sizes of the two circles?

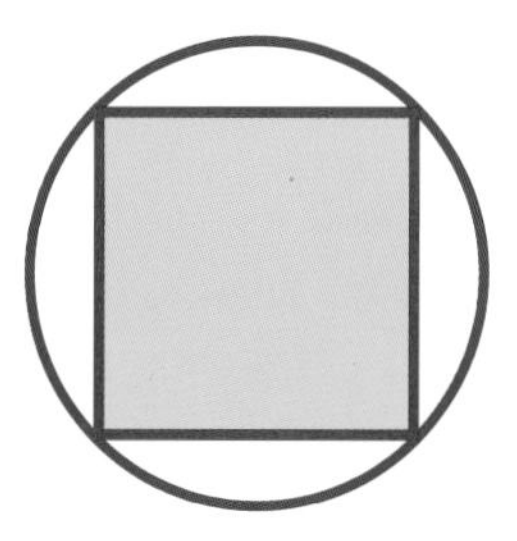

A

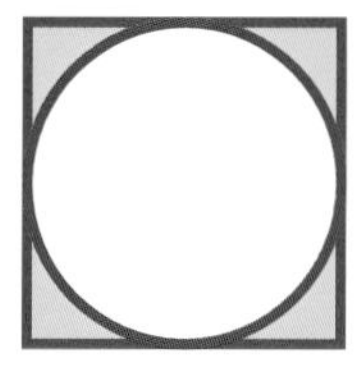

B

The Coloured Pyramid

A regular pyramid has four faces that are equilateral triangles and each one is painted either red, blue, green or yellow. The pyramid is rotated and these four different bird's-eye views are made by looking down on each of its four corners.

Which one of the views is incorrect?

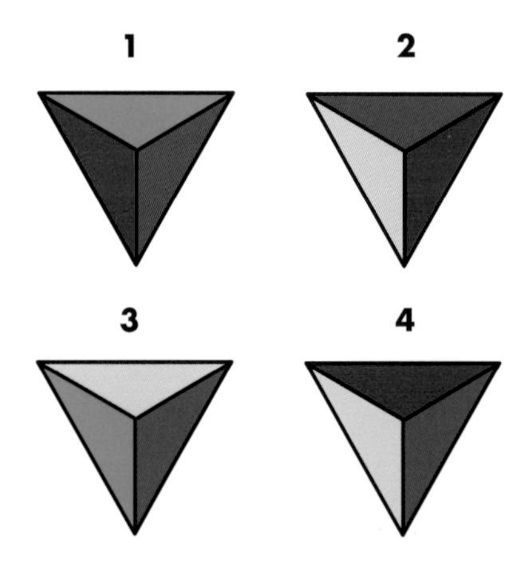

Splitting The Rainbow

The colours of the rainbow are arranged with white around a circular disk (shown below) so that each colour occupies one of the eight segments. A colour cannot be seen next to or opposite a colour that it is next to in the rainbow. Where does white go?

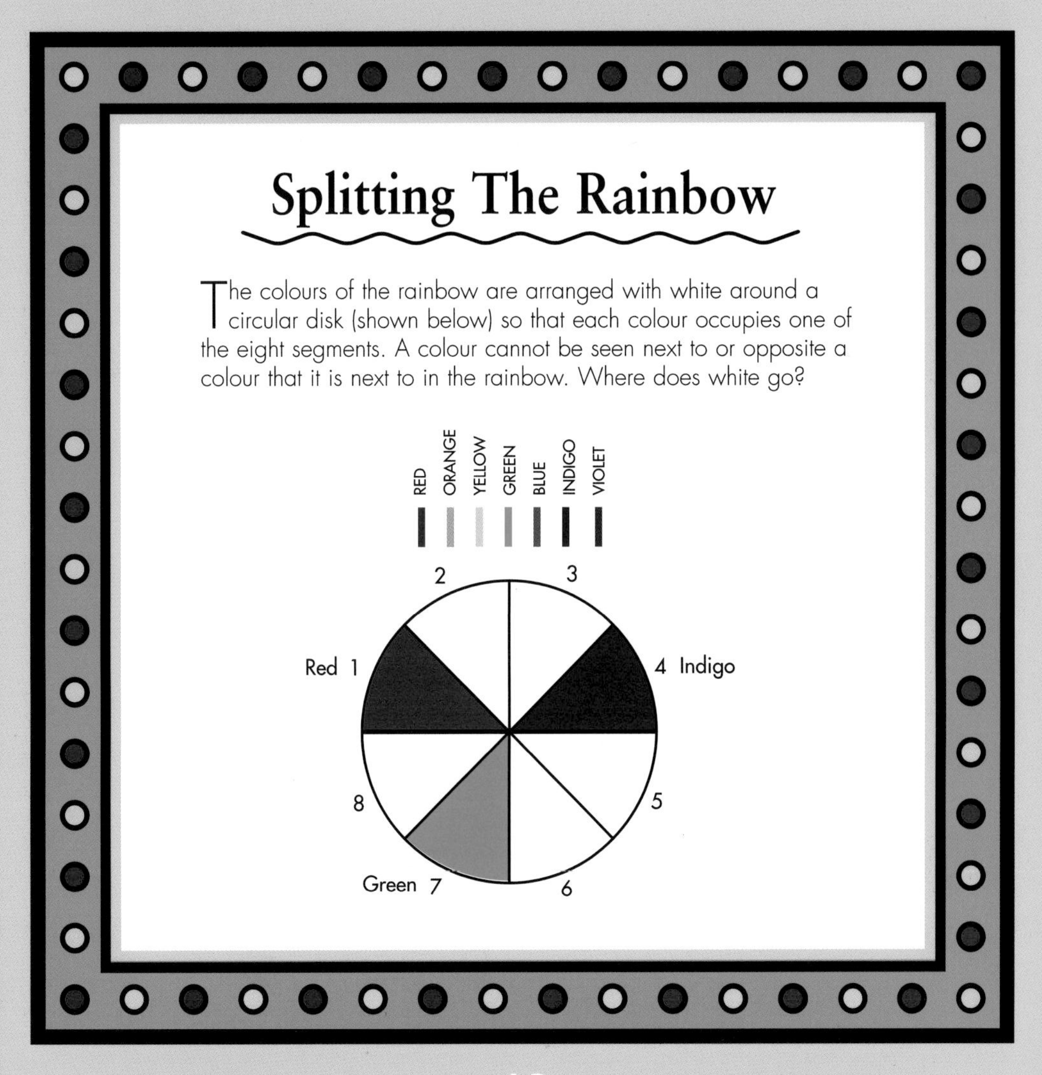

Animal Farm

Each of these animals has a very peculiar weight - not at all what you would imagine. Can you work out from the balanced see-saws below, how many cats will balance one cow?

Up The Garden Path

Mr Wilson has a large garden of which he is extremely proud, and through this garden he has laid gravel paths about which he is very particular. Find a way for him to re-gravel his paths without going over the same piece of path more than once and never venturing onto the well-kept lawn.

Olympic Fun And Games

To celebrate great sporting events, in particular the Olympics, the Marathon Committee designed a special marathon, to be run 26 miles and 385 yards around a very special course (see below). So many people wanted to enter that the judges were afraid of people being lapped, and accidents occurring.

Can you work out a route so that athletes need never run any stretch twice, cross their own tracks, or leave the course?

Lord's Legacy

A rich old man dies and leaves each of his four spoilt sons a cottage on his 600yd by 600yd estate. Not only do they fight about how to share his square estate into four identical parts, but each one also wants a stretch of land at least long enough for a 400yd golf driving range - how do they manage this?

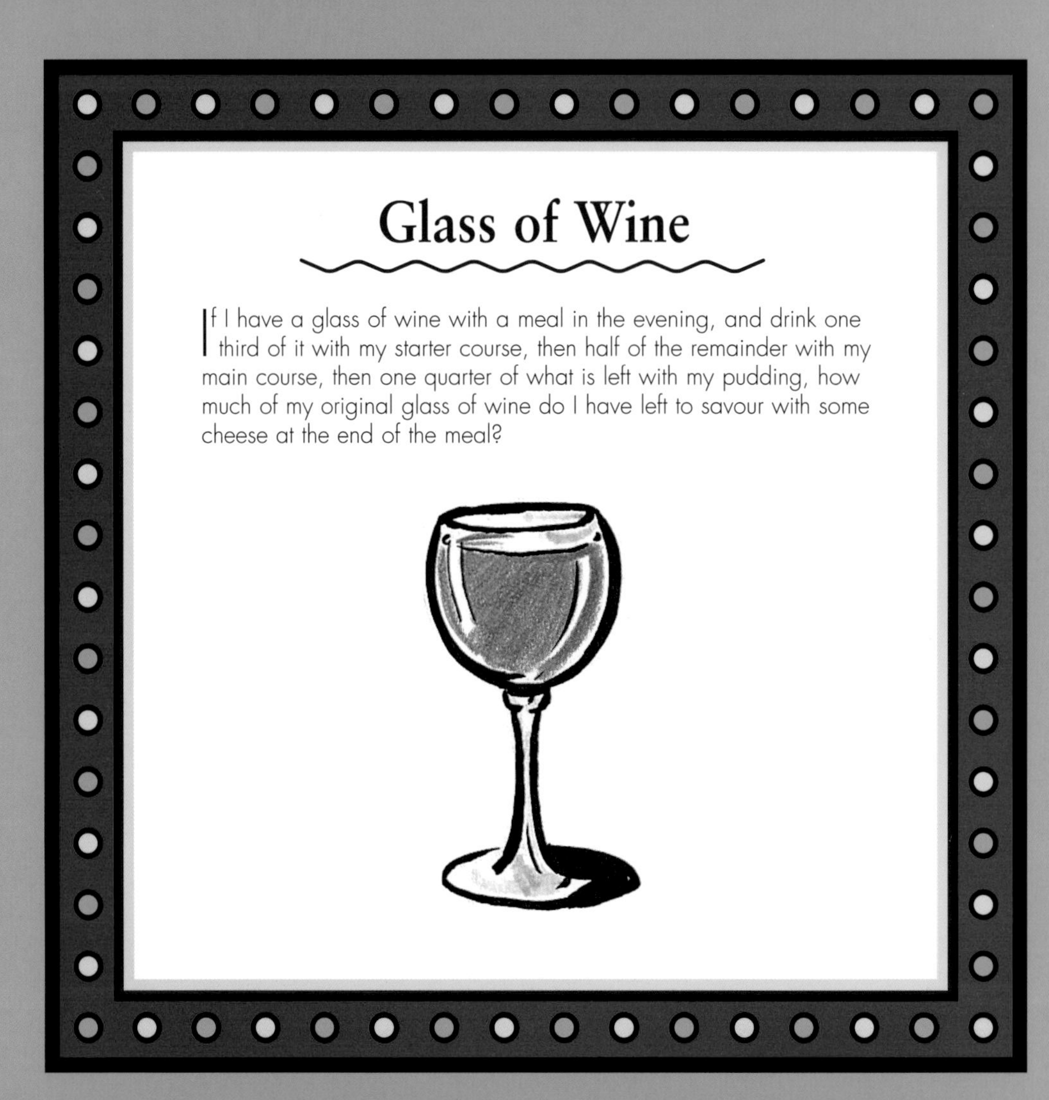

Glass of Wine

If I have a glass of wine with a meal in the evening, and drink one third of it with my starter course, then half of the remainder with my main course, then one quarter of what is left with my pudding, how much of my original glass of wine do I have left to savour with some cheese at the end of the meal?

Dice Dilemma

Jenny has been given a game for her birthday, but before she can begin to play, the dice has to be made by folding the shape below. When it's folded it will look like one, but only one, of the dice shown.

Which one?

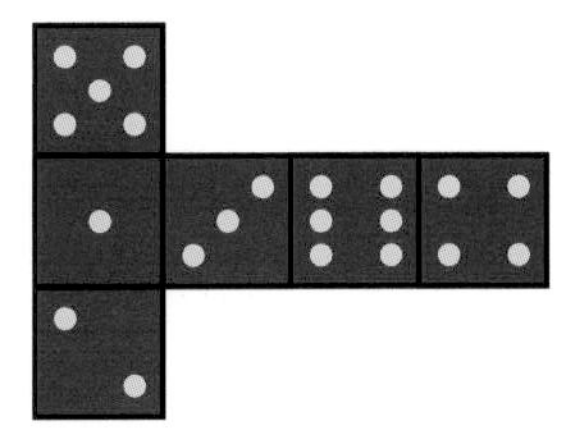

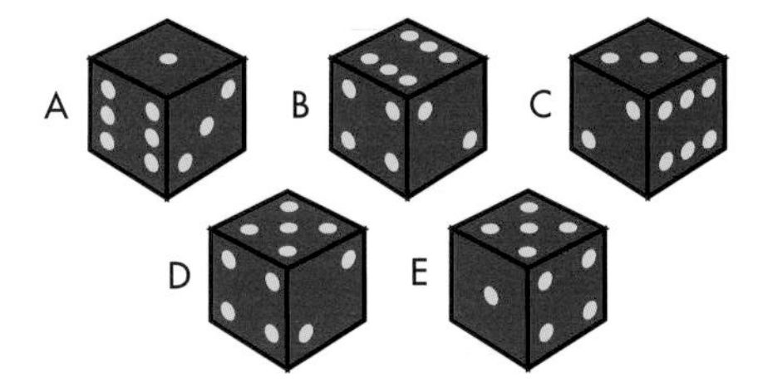

Price Poser

You spend £21 in the off licence. The whisky cost twice as much as the beer, which cost twice as much as the soda water.

How much was the beer?

The Young Adventurer

A young adventurer needs to make a difficult journey from one enchanted tree to another which is on an island in the middle of a treacherous circular lake. He cannot swim across, as this lake has a strong clockwise current which would sweep him away. The trees are 50 metres apart and all he has to help him is a length of rope, just short of 110 metres long. How can he reach the magic tree without endangering his life?

Tankard

You have three tankards which hold respectively eight pints, five pints and three pints. There are no measurements on these tankards, so the only exact quantities you can know are 'full' and 'empty'. The tankard which holds eight pints is filled with liquid. Find the most efficient way, using these three tankards, to end up with exactly four pints of this liquid in each of the two larger tankards.

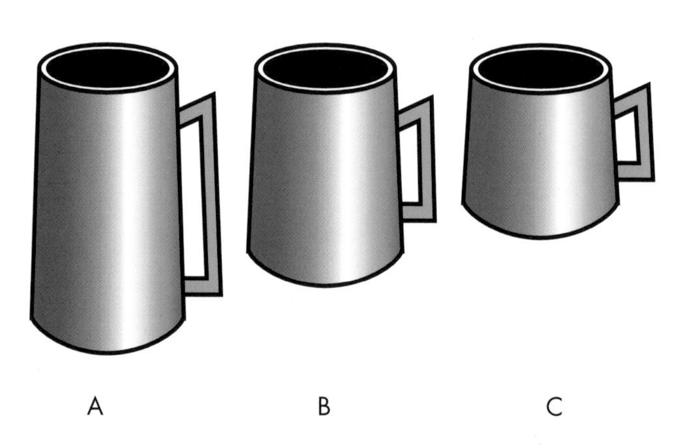

Putter Problems

George has bought a putter for his son's birthday. As Paul lives some distance away, George plans to post it to him, but finds the Post Office will not accept parcels longer than 70cm or taller than 50cm, and the putter measures 95cm in length. However, George thinks of a way of packing it so that it conforms to the Post Office regulations. How?

Triangular Tricks

How many triangles can you count in this picture?

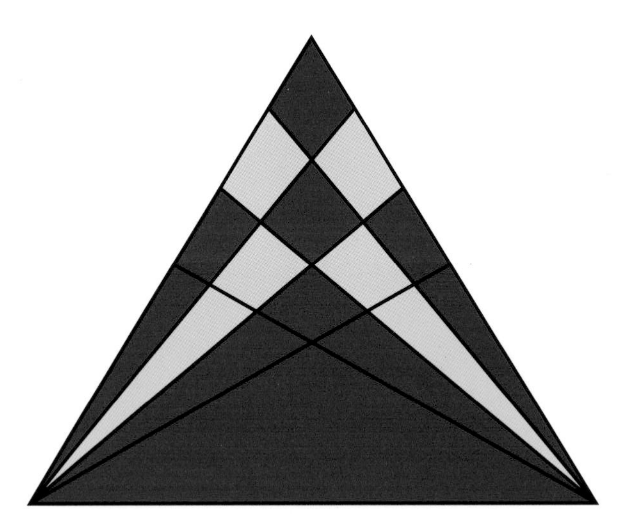

Meet Your Match

15 matches are laid on a table so as to form five equal squares. Remove three matches to leave only three squares.

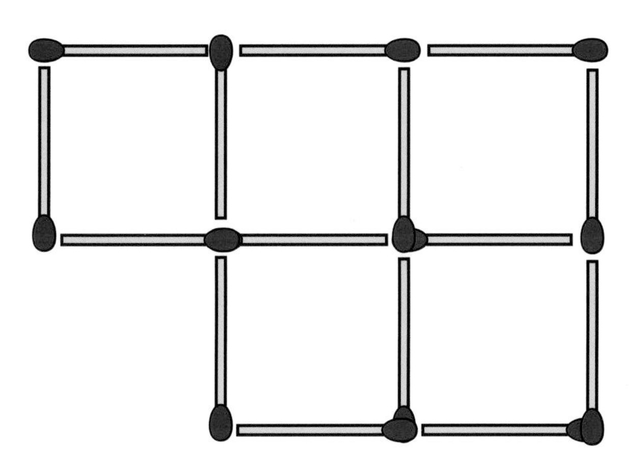

Odd One Out

Which is the odd one out of the following illustrations?

Farmer Giles

Farmer Giles wants to keep livestock in all of his fields. He would prefer just cows, or perhaps cows and sheep, but local health regulations decree that he is not allowed to keep the same type of animal in any two adjoining fields. What is the fewest number of animal types he will require to fill the fields and abide by the regulations?

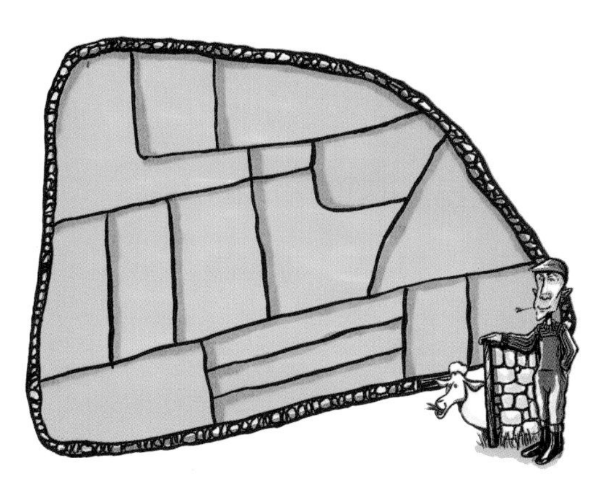

Clever Cogs

If there was a weight attached to the bottom cog of this sequence, and a lever attached to the top one which started the cog moving anti-clockwise, would the weight at the bottom move up or down?

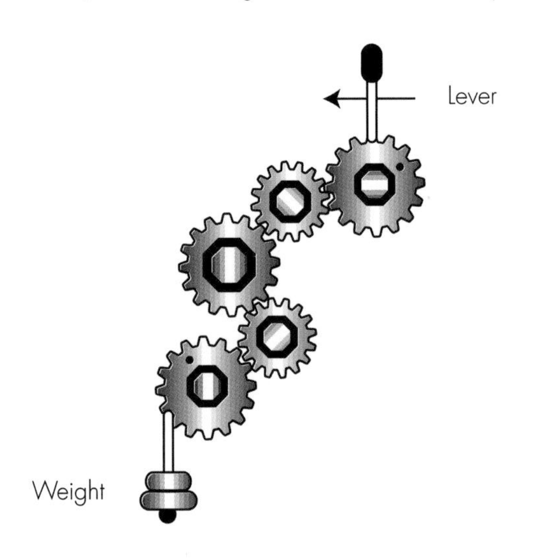

Apples, Oranges And Pears

On three separate trips to the greengrocers the following combinations of fruit were purchased for the total cost shown. The price of each fruit did not change. What is the total cost of an apple, an orange and a pear?

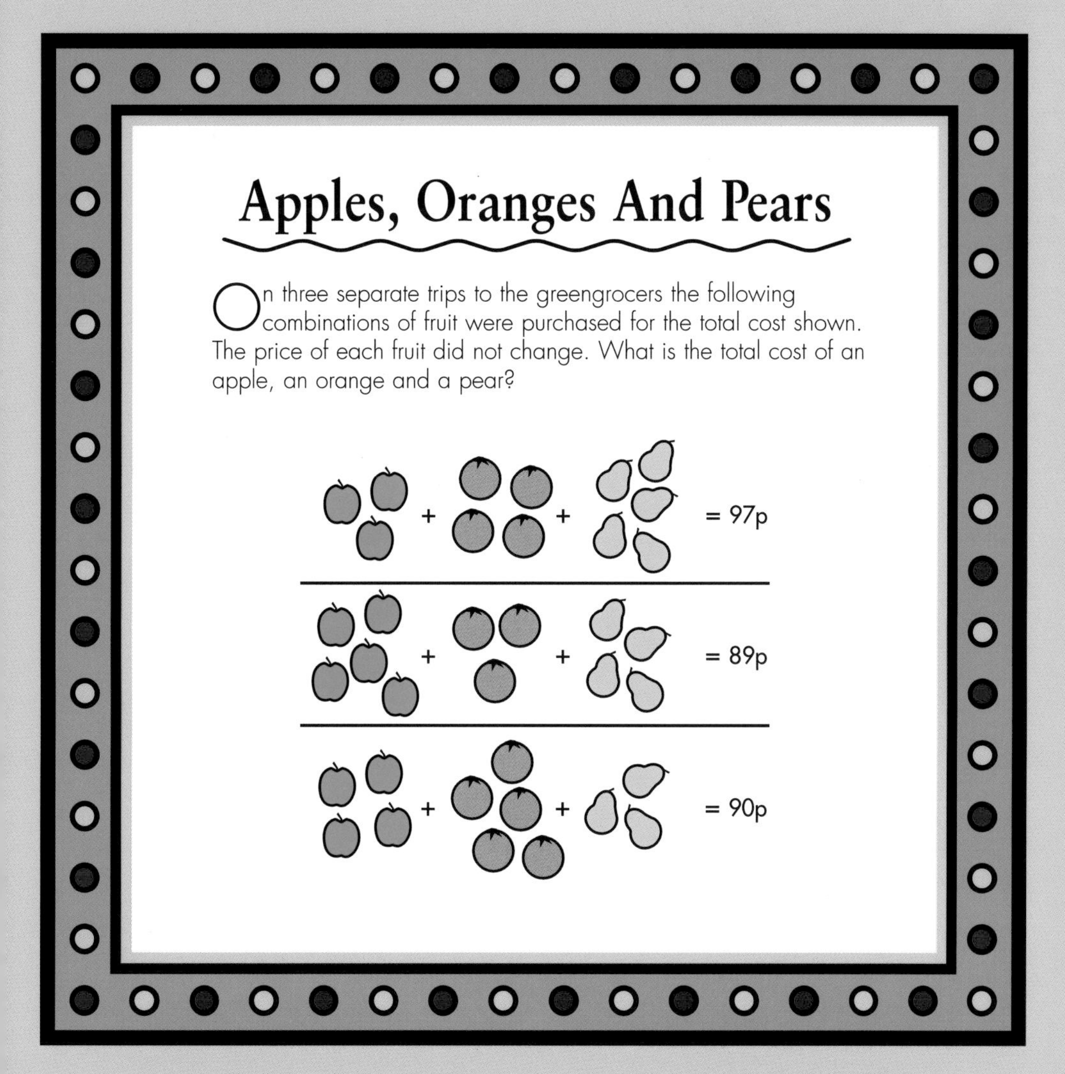

Artistic Licence

An artist is painting on a large canvas measuring two metres by two metres. He wants to cover half the canvas in a deep, rich purple, but he also likes the large scale of the painting, and wants to keep a square section which is still two metres high and two metres wide. Is there any way that he can have both?

A Classic One

Harry Stotle, teacher of classics, was meeting his new class for their first Latin lesson. After they had all introduced themselves, Harry said that James was the odd one out. Why?

Breakfast Blues

Mr and Mrs Greengage are setting up a bed and breakfast business. They need to buy a new coffee-pot, and want to buy one which holds a large volume of liquid.

Out of the two below, which one should they buy, and why?

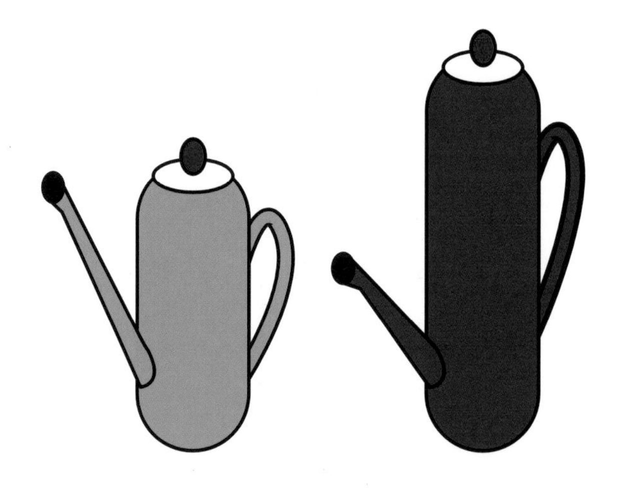

Tower Block

What is the value of the dots on the hidden faces of the dice below?

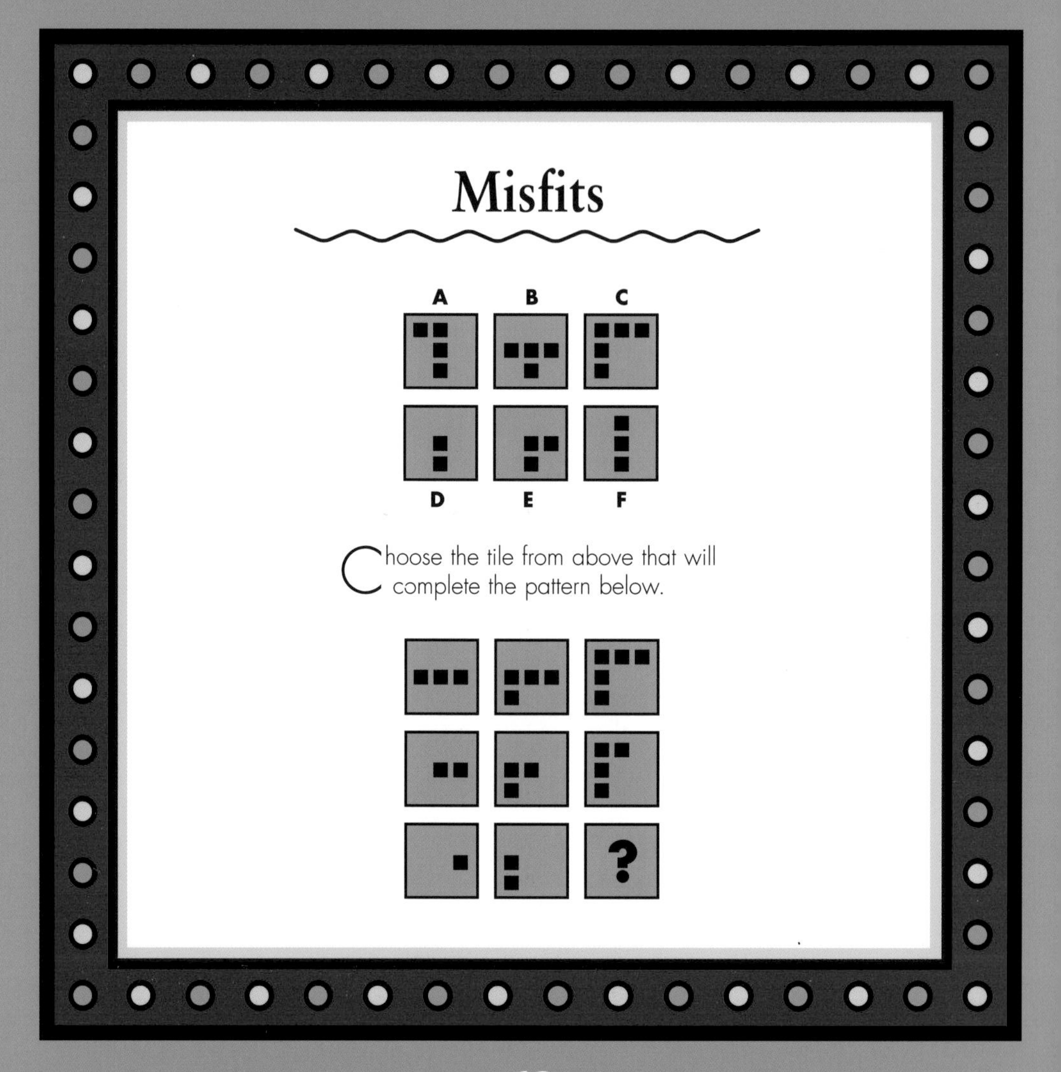
Misfits
A
B
C
D
E
F
Choose the tile from above that will complete the pattern below.
?

Alcoholics Anonymous

Below are four equations and a fifth one which needs completing.

Can you choose the alcoholic beverage which will balance the fifth equation?

Matchmaker

Can you move just two matches in the arrangement below and make seven squares?

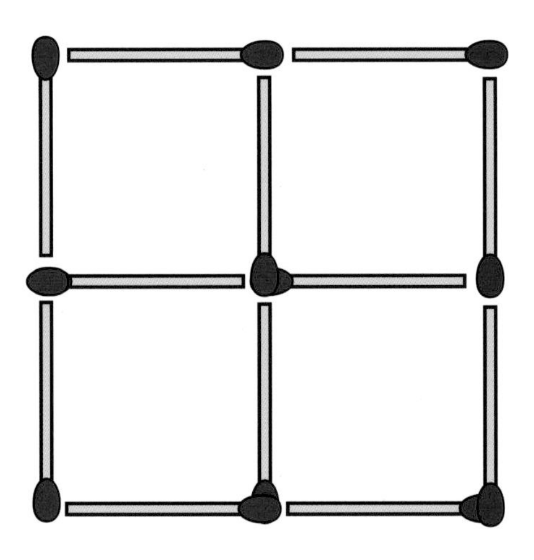

Bits And Pieces

Can you divide this shape into four pieces of the same shape and size?

Get Knotted

Terry has just joined the Boy Scouts, and has been learning how to tie various knots.

This is one of Terry's knots. If you pulled both ends of the string, would it turn into a knot, or pull apart?

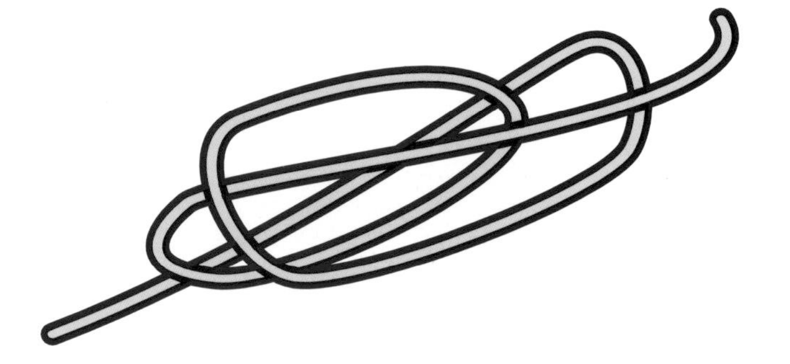

Codeword

In terms of a code, this is elementary. Can you crack the code and explain how it works?

FMFNFOUBSZ

Building Blocks

The circumference of each log below is two feet. If the logs were rolled forward until they had made one whole revolution, how far forward would the block of stone have moved?

Against The Tide

Below you can see a fish made from matches with a coin for an eye, which is swimming from right to left. Move the coin and just three matches and make the fish swim in the other direction.

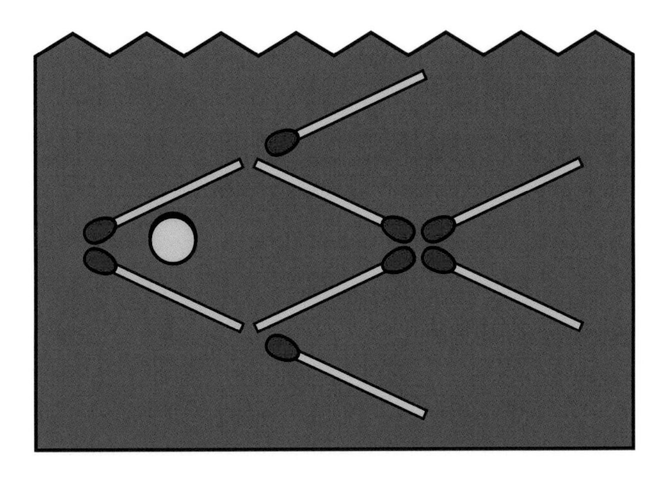

Solutions

Page 1 ~ Matchstick Tricks

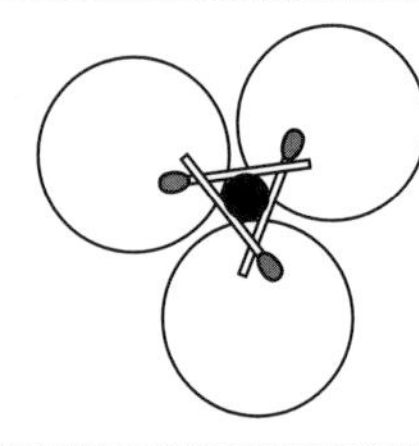

Page 2 ~ Sheep

By placing the pens as shown at right

Page 3 ~ Dinner Party

Jennie's evening-wear was ruined.

Solutions

Page 4 ~ Caged Cats

By placing the pens as shown to the right.

Page 5 ~ Prison Poser

This is one solution. He could put two inmates in each corner cell.

Page 6 ~ Robotics

Paul. Whenever Robbo comes to a red and blue square together, he must pass through them with the blue square on his left.

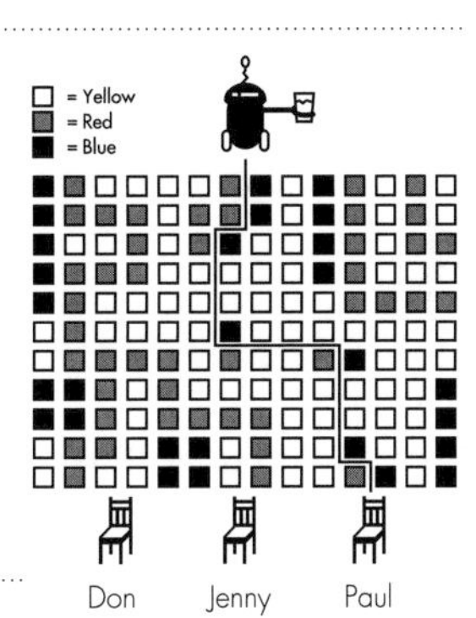

Solutions

Page 7 ~ Shop 'Till You Drop

Joanna spent $930.

Page 8 ~ Squares Before Your Eyes

There are 204 squares on a draughts board.

1 (8x8)
4 (7x7)
9 (6x6)
16 (5x5)
25 (4x4)
36 (3x3)
49 (2x2)
64 (1x1)

204

Page 9 ~ Name The Gnome

Ruby. The consonants of the name are represented by the initial letters of the colours of the hat and suit at the beginning and end of the name. The second letter is a vowel, a,e,i,o,u in order, leaving u to be used.

Solutions

Page 10 ~ Cubed

D.

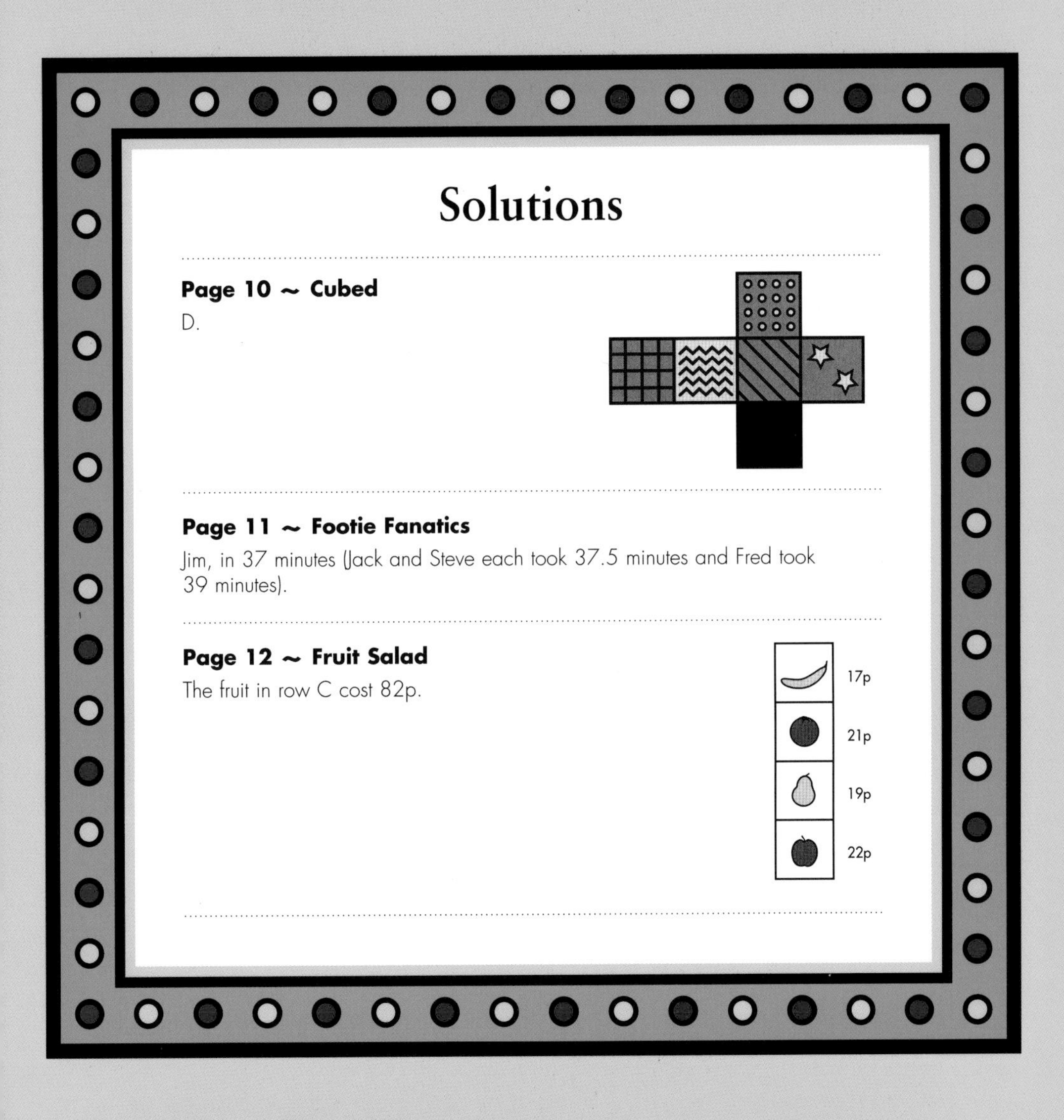

Page 11 ~ Footie Fanatics

Jim, in 37 minutes (Jack and Steve each took 37.5 minutes and Fred took 39 minutes).

Page 12 ~ Fruit Salad

The fruit in row C cost 82p.

Solutions

Page 13 ~ Snookered

At point C. Draw a line from the red ball, perpendicular to the cushion, and extend beyond the edge of the snooker table the same distance as the red ball is from the cushion. Call this new point R1(i.e. red ball to cushion = cushion to R1). Now join the white ball to R1. This straight line is the shortest distance from the white ball to R1, cutting the cushion at C, so white to C to R1 = white to C to red.

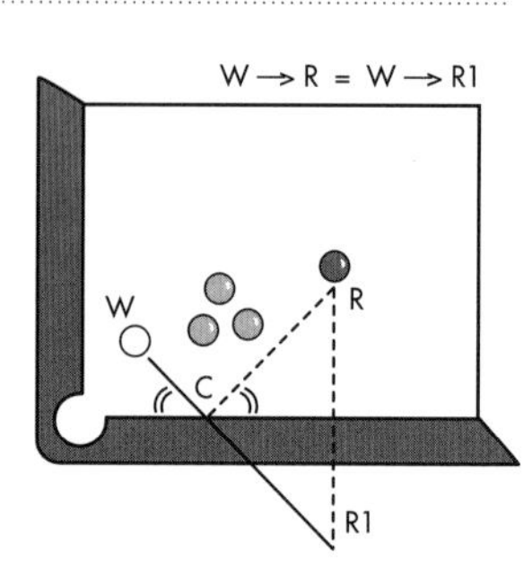

Page 14 ~ Crack The Code

F.

Page 15 ~ Lines For Coins

Nine 'through lines'

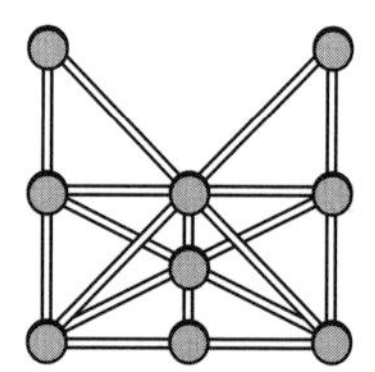

Solutions

Page 16 ~ Name That Card

The two of hearts. From the top right the cards jump a number and alternate through the suits (see right).

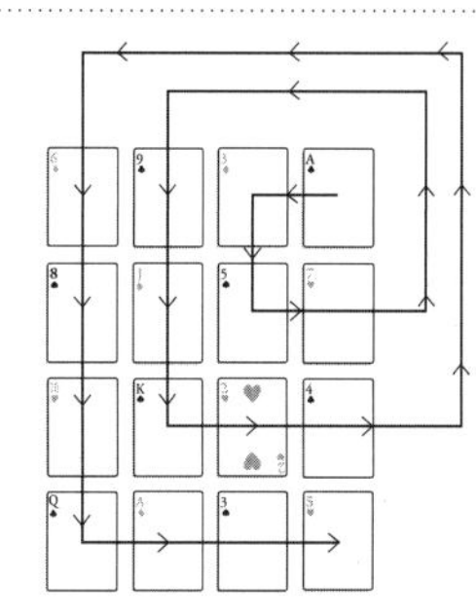

Page 17 ~ Game, Set And Match

Move the top match up slightly.

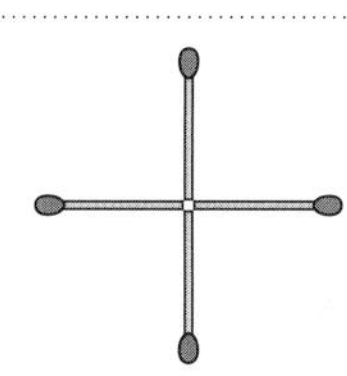

Page 18 ~ Hard Currency

Bill's pint cost £1.80.

The values of the tokens are:

= £1 = 50p

= 20p = 10p

Solutions

Page 19 ~ Four Towns

D.

Page 20 ~ Tiling The Wall

Eleven.

One tile in the middle row and five in each of the outside rows.

Page 21 ~ A Fruity Number

54.

Solutions

Page 22 ~ Cabbage Conundrums

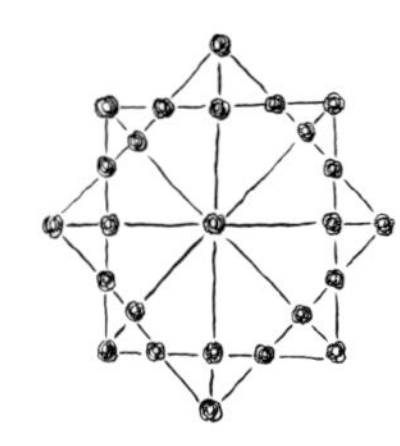

Page 23 ~ Birthday Blues

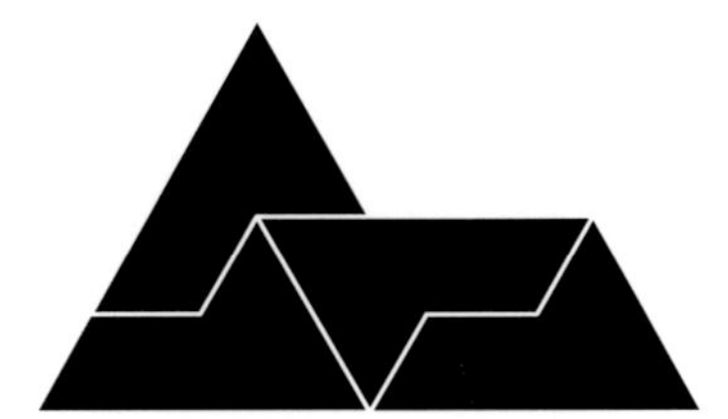

Page 24 ~ Remove The Weight

Step 1 ~ move 1lb to the left-hand pan and add 2lb to the right-hand pan.
Step 2 ~ move 1lb to the right-hand pan and add 2lb to the left-hand pan.
Step 3 ~ move 2lb to the right-hand pan and add 4lb to the left-hand pan.
Step 4 ~ move 4lb to the right-hand pan and remove 8lb.

Solutions

Page 25 ~ Ice And A Slice

Slide the horizontal straw to one side by half its length, then move the unattached straw to form the remaining side of the cocktail glass.

Page 26 ~ The Green Jigsaw Puzzle

Piece C does not belong.

Page 27 ~ Water Lilies

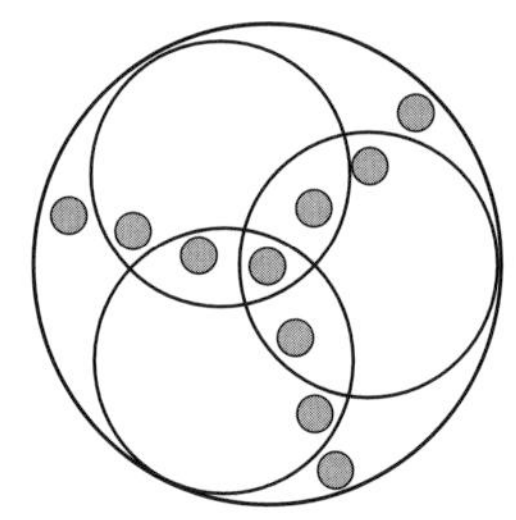

Solutions

Page 28 ~ Chop Suey

Page 29 ~ Hexamania

27 hexagons.

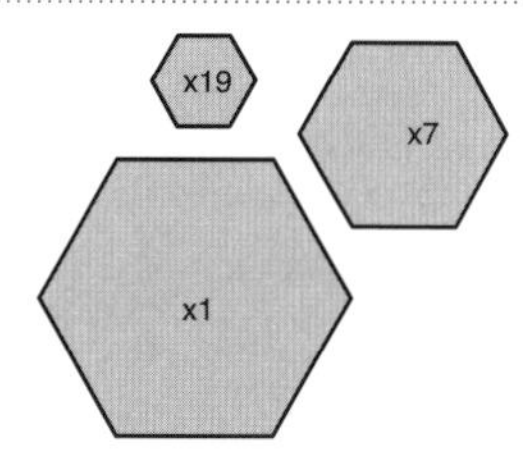

Page 30 ~ Multi-dots

3. The two adjacent smaller numbers are multiplied together to make the next larger number.

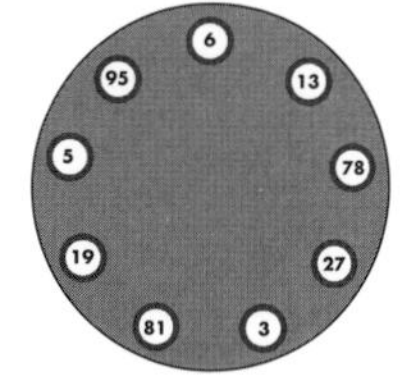

Solutions

Page 31 ~ Crazy Cogs

Yes.

C and D turn clockwise and B turns counter-clockwise.

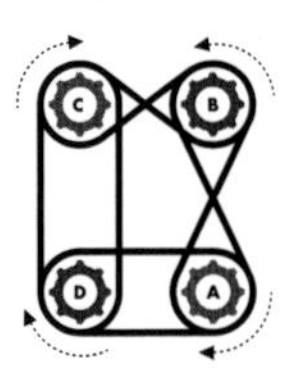

Page 32 ~ Crown Jewels

If John had a girlfriend he would have spent £204.

Page 33 ~ Extensions

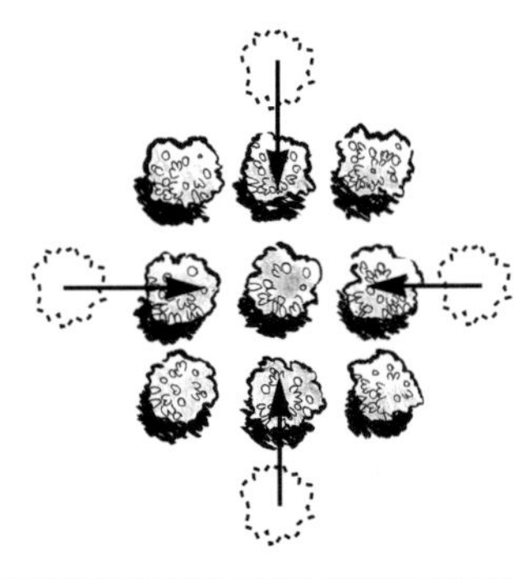

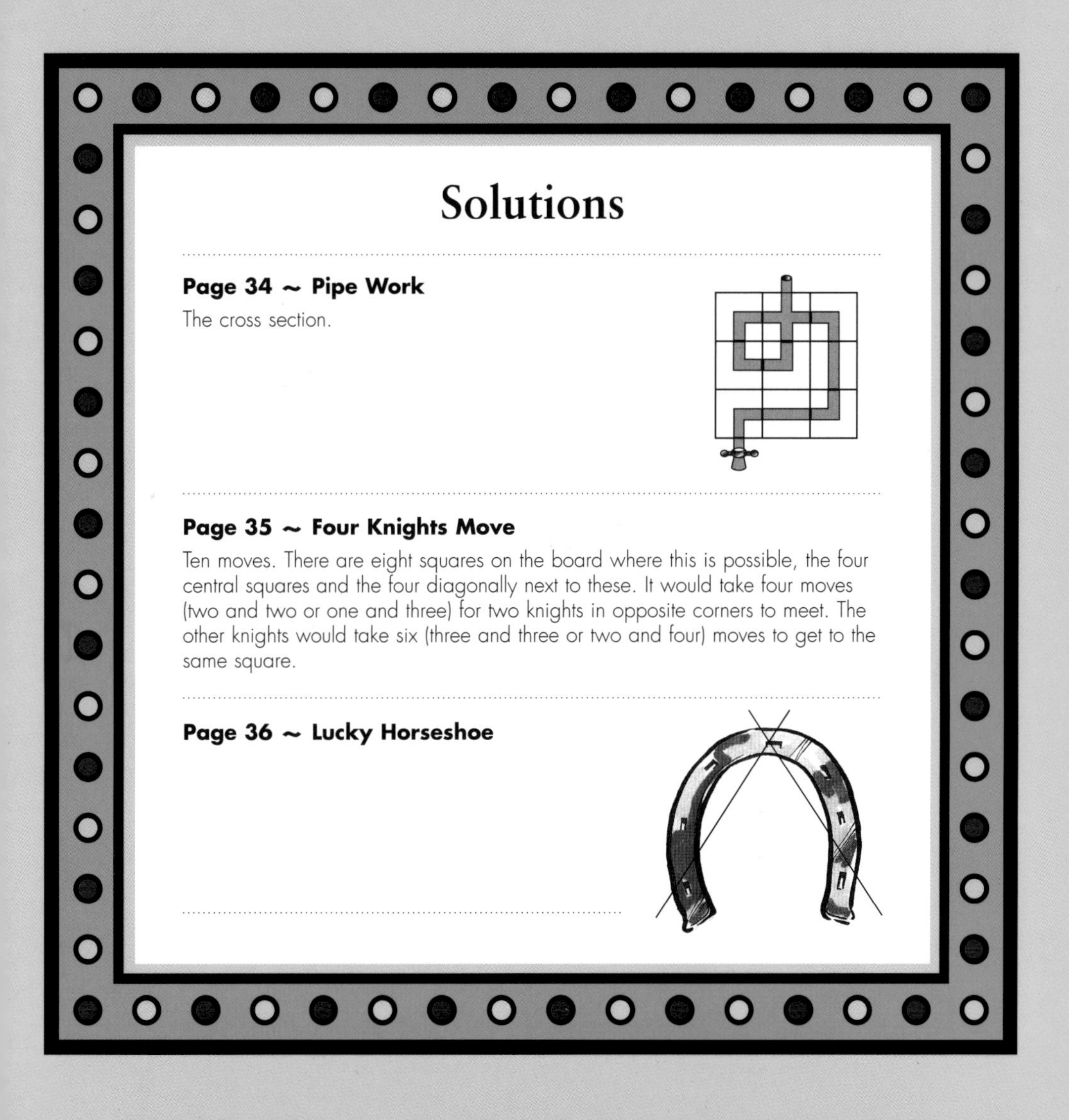

Solutions

Page 34 ~ Pipe Work

The cross section.

Page 35 ~ Four Knights Move

Ten moves. There are eight squares on the board where this is possible, the four central squares and the four diagonally next to these. It would take four moves (two and two or one and three) for two knights in opposite corners to meet. The other knights would take six (three and three or two and four) moves to get to the same square.

Page 36 ~ Lucky Horseshoe

Solutions

Page 37 ~ Water Trough

The 20cm bung.

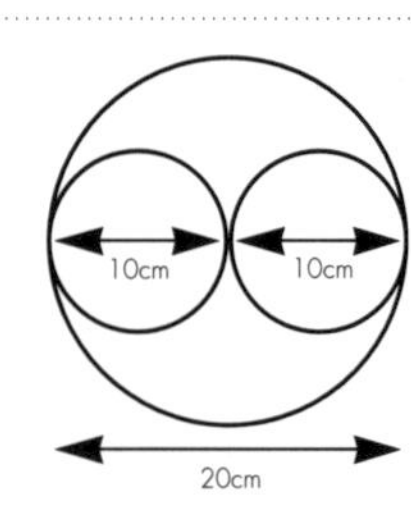

Page 38 ~ Mole

The boys' code was simple.
They wrote out the alphabet like this:

A B C D E F G H I J K L M
Z Y X W V U T S R Q P O N

and then wrote their message by transposing the required letter with the one above or below it.

1 I	N	■	2 T	H	E
3 S	P	O	R	T	S
■	4 H	A	L	L	■
5 A	F	T	E	R	■
■	6 L	U	N	C	H

Page 39 ~ Chain Reaction

Yes. If they undid all three links of one of the broken sections, they could use these three to join the others together.

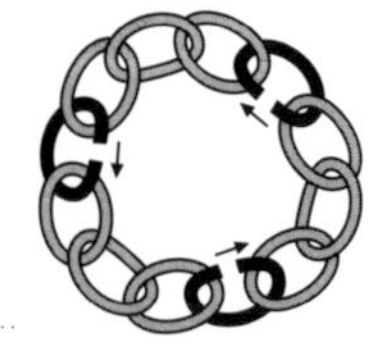

Solutions

Page 40 ~ Square The Circle

The circle in A is twice the area of the circle in B.

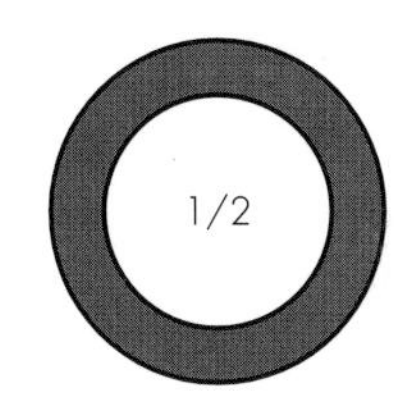

Page 41 ~ The Coloured Pyramid

View 2 is incorrect.

The views in 2 and 4 both have green as the base, therefore 1 and 3 must be correct. From view 3, looking at the top right-hand corner with green as the base, the correct colours are red, blue, yellow, which is the same as view 4, which means that view 2 is incorrect.

Page 42 ~ Splitting The Rainbow

Between red and green.

Blue and yellow are next to green in the rainbow and therefore can only occupy 2 and 5. Blue cannot occupy 5 because it is next to indigo, so 2 must be blue and 5 must be yellow. Violet cannot be next to or opposite indigo and therefore must be in 6. Orange cannot be next to red in 8, so 8 must be white.

Solutions

Page 43 ~ Animal Farm

Five cats balance one cow.

If cat + cow	**=**	**dog**
	=	**2 cats + horse**
		[from top two see-saws]
3 dogs	**=**	**3 x (2 cats + horse)**
3 dogs	**=**	**6 cats + 3 horses**
If 2 dogs	**=**	**3 horses**
		[from bottom see-saw],
then 1 dog	**=**	**6 cats**
cat + cow	**=**	**6 cats**
cow	**=**	**6 cats – cat**
	=	**5 cats**

Page 44 ~ Up The Garden Path

This is one solution.

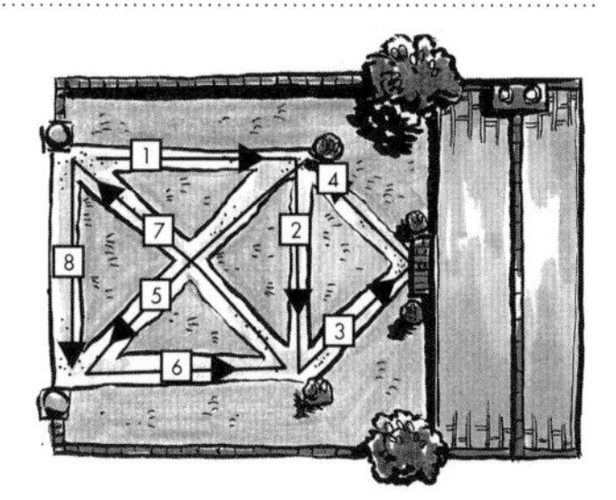

Page 45 ~ Olympic Fun And Games

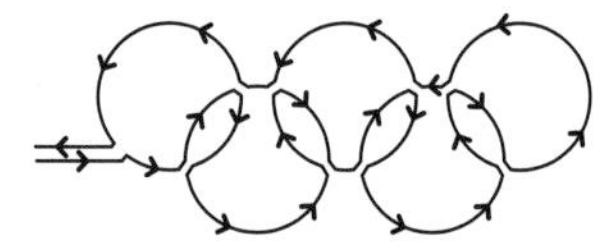

Solutions

Page 46 ~ Lord's Legacy

Page 47 ~ Glass of Wine

One quarter of my glass of wine.
1 – 4/12 = 8/12
Half of 8/12 is 4/12
One quarter off this leaves 3/12 in the glass, which is one quarter of the original amount.

Page 48 ~ Dice Dilemma

C.

Solutions

Page 49 ~ Price Poser

£6. If the soda is X, the beer is 2X and the whisky is 4X.
If 7X =£21, X =3.

Page 50 ~ The Young Adventurer

He should tie one end of the rope to the tree on the shore, then walk around the lake holding the other end, until he comes back to the original tree and ties the rope on again. The adventurer could pull himself through the water to the island to reach the second enchanted tree.

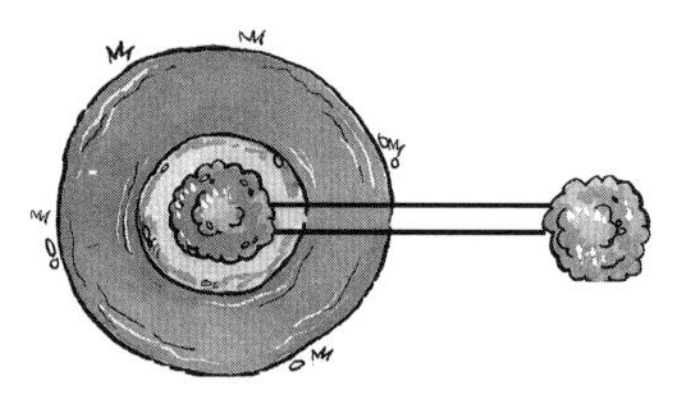

Page 51 ~ Tankard

	A (8) pints	B (5) pints	C (3) pints
Start	8	0	0
1.	3	5	0
2.	3	2	3
3.	6	2	0
4.	6	0	2
5.	1	5	2
6.	1	4	3
7.	4	4	0

Solutions

Page 52 ~ Putter Problems

George places it diagonally
in a box that measures 70cm square.

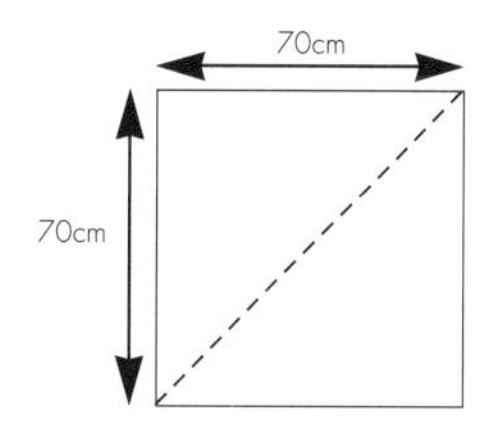

Page 53 ~ Triangular Tricks

64.

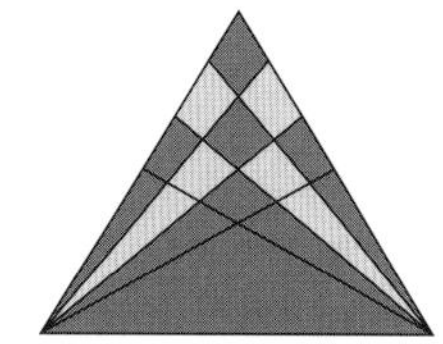

Page 54 ~ Meet Your Match

Take one match from the middle top row and the two matches which form the bottom right hand corner.

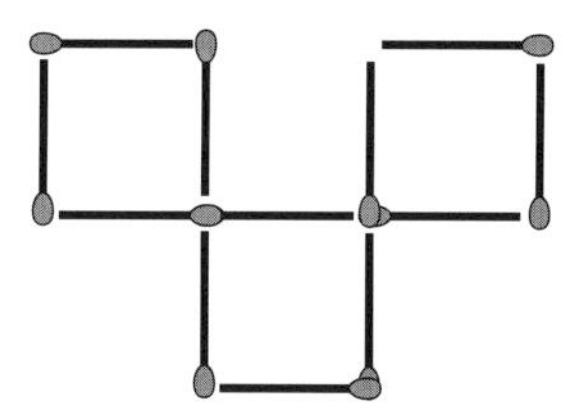

Solutions

Page 55 ~ Odd One Out

E. This is a left hand – all the others are right hands or feet.

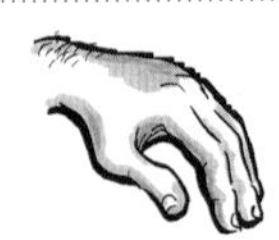

Page 56 ~ Farmer Giles

He needs four different types of animal.

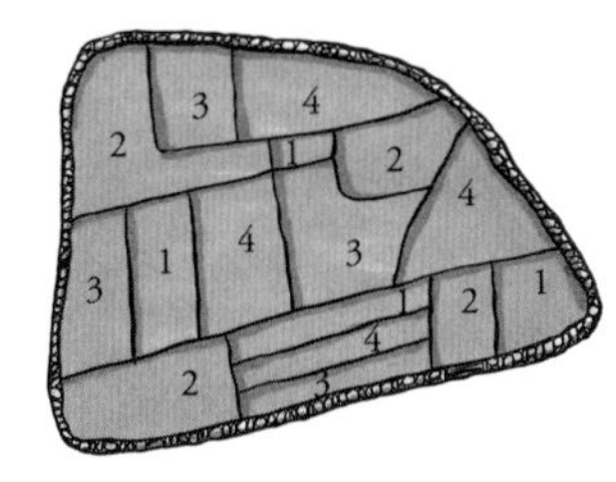

Page 57 ~ Clever Cogs

The weight at the bottom would move down.

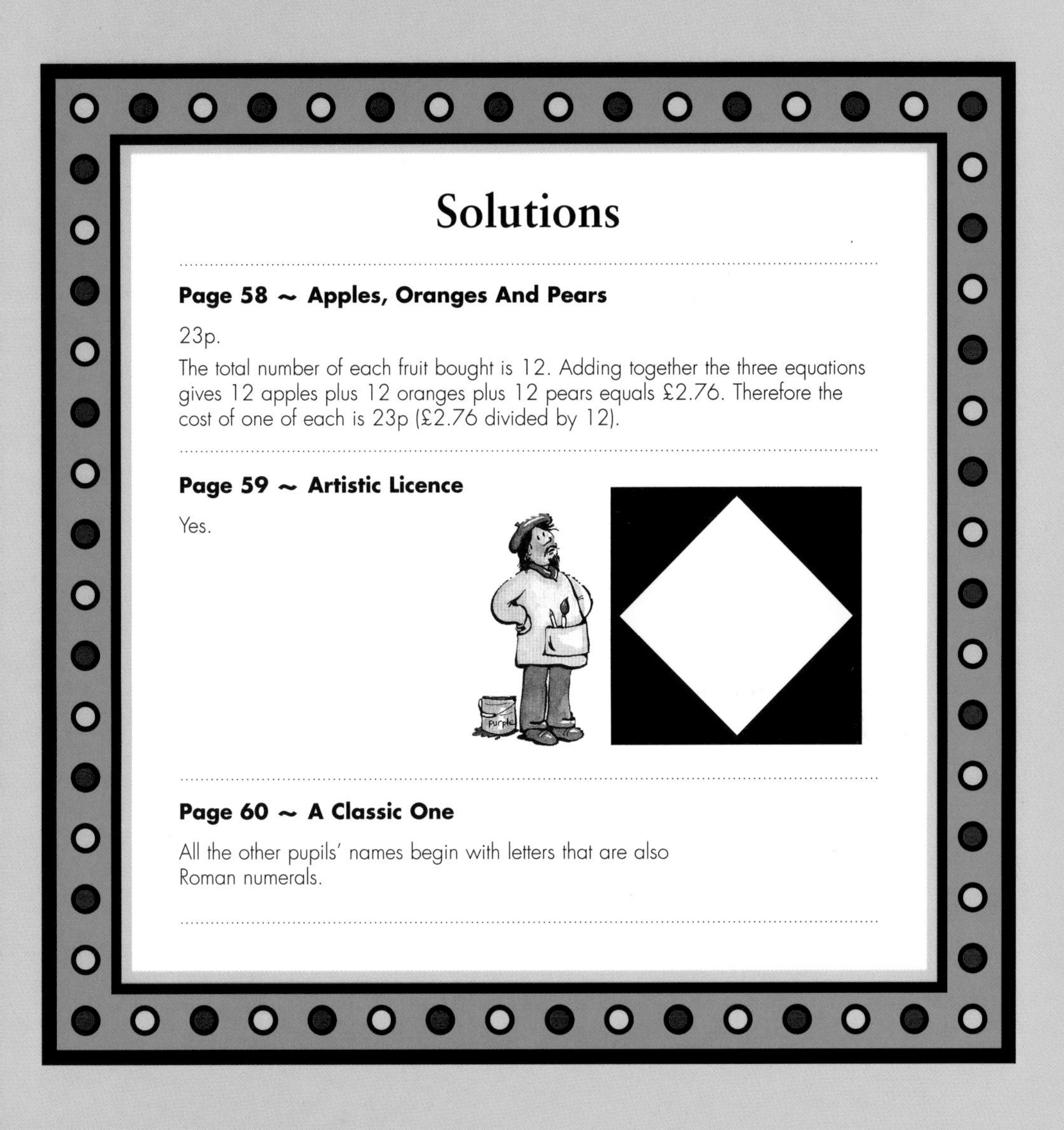

Solutions

Page 58 ~ Apples, Oranges And Pears

23p.

The total number of each fruit bought is 12. Adding together the three equations gives 12 apples plus 12 oranges plus 12 pears equals £2.76. Therefore the cost of one of each is 23p (£2.76 divided by 12).

Page 59 ~ Artistic Licence

Yes.

Page 60 ~ A Classic One

All the other pupils' names begin with letters that are also Roman numerals.

Solutions

Page 61 ~ Breakfast Blues

The shorter coffee-pot will contain the most coffee. Its spout extends to the height of the pot, which means it can be filled to the top, whereas the larger coffee-pot has a shorter spout which will overflow as soon as the pot is filled above this level.

Page 62 ~ Tower Block

39.

Page 63 ~ Misfits

F.

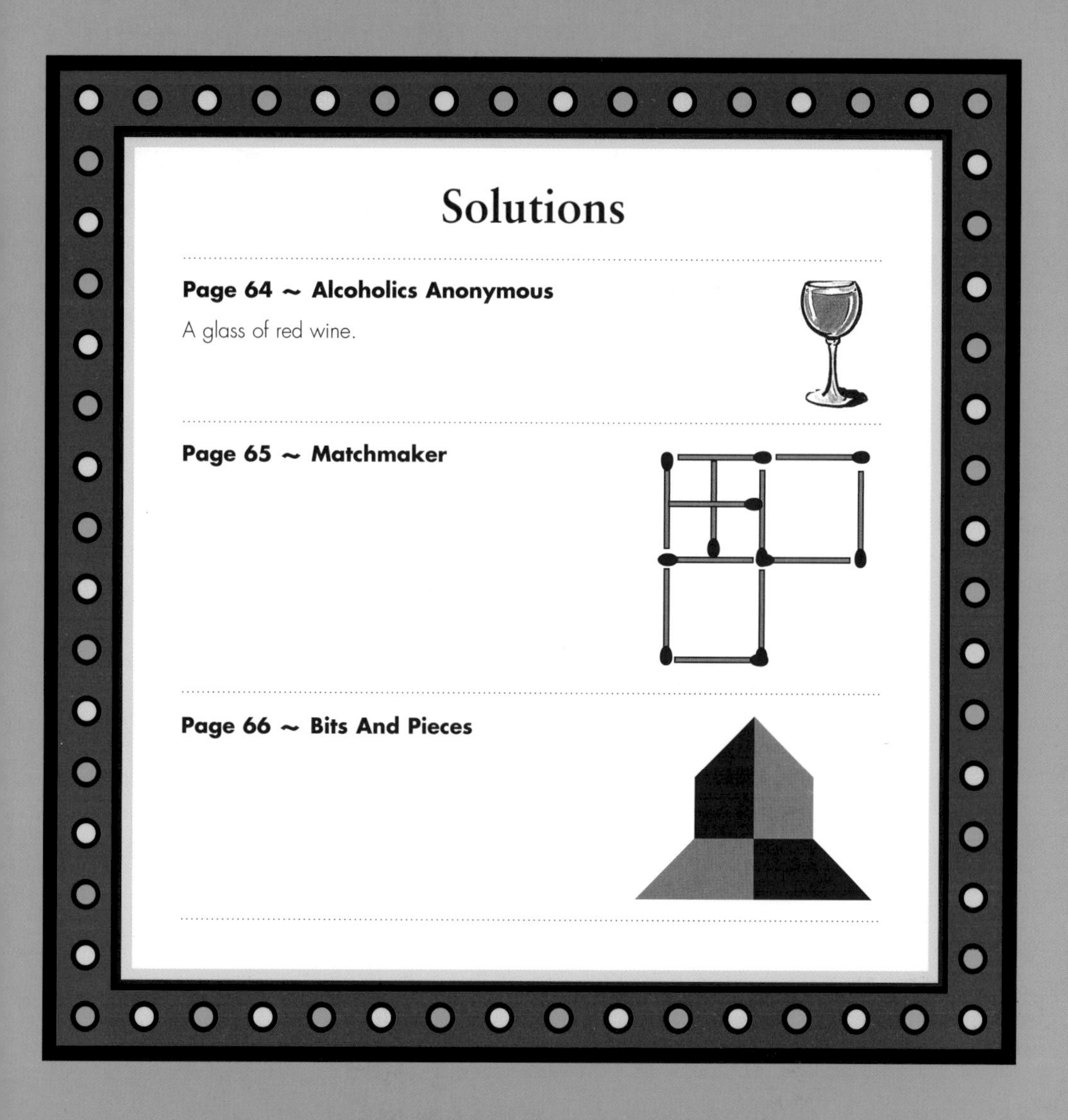

Solutions

Page 64 ~ Alcoholics Anonymous

A glass of red wine.

Page 65 ~ Matchmaker

Page 66 ~ Bits And Pieces

Solutions

Page 67 ~ Get Knotted

It would pull apart.

Page 68 ~ Codeword

It spells elementary.
Each letter represents the letter before.

E L E M E N T A R Y

Page 69 ~ Building Blocks

Four feet. As each log is rolled forward, its contact point with the stone goes backward along the stone. One complete revolution will end up with the log two feet further back than the stone. The log is also in contact with the ground, and one complete revolution will take it two feet forward along the ground. Therefore the stone will move four feet forward.

Page 70 ~ Against The Tide

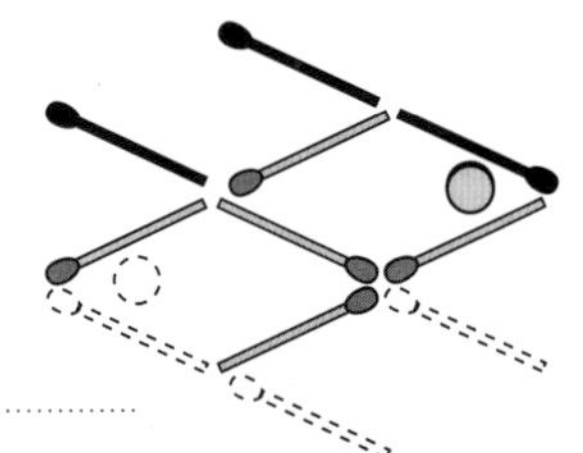